THE BOOK OF JEWISH HUMOR

Other Books by Rufus Learsi

The Book of
JEWISH HUMOR

Stories of the Wise Men of Chelem and
Other Tales Assembled and Retold

by

Rufus Learsi, pseud. of

Israel Goldberg

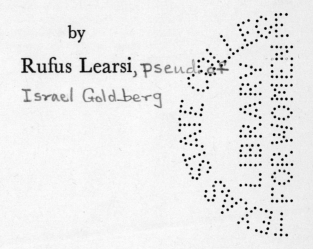

NEW YORK
BLOCH PUBLISHING COMPANY
"The Jewish Book Concern"
1941

MANUFACTURED IN THE UNITED STATES OF AMERICA
BY THE HADDON CRAFTSMEN, INC., CAMDEN, N. J.

TO KALMAN WHITEMAN

Philosopher, colleague and friend

CONTENTS

FOREWORD

The tales in this compilation have been told and retold for generations. Embodying the humor of a race, they possess the rich flavor of folklore and mirror a people that knows how to laugh at its own foibles and mishaps. Nor are they without pathos, for the life out of which they spring is stamped with penury and persecution, and with that exuberance of mind which engenders sadness as well as understanding.

In the present retelling, the author has seen fit to add to the tales of Chelem a number that have not been heretofore identified with that famous nursery of wisdom, but which have appeared to him to deserve the honor. He is indebted to many sources out of which he singles out the work of Immanuel Olsvanger and Alexander Moszkowski for special acknowledgment. For many of them, also, he is grateful to his friend Bernard Semel who adds to his other attainments the gift of humor and the skill of the accomplished raconteur.

R. L.

THE WISE MEN OF CHELEM

How Chelem Rose Up and Flourished

THE BIRTH OF CHELEM

History loves to linger over the beginnings of memorable places; and the city of Chelem, whose people became renowned through all the earth for their incredible wisdom, is no exception. The traditions of Chelem relate that before the work of building began, the founders met in solemn assembly and deliberated a long time on the best site for their city. They decided finally to build it at the foot of a mountain.

The great day arrived and the builders began by climbing to the summit where they cut down trees for their houses. But how were the logs to be brought down, seeing the Chelemites had no vehicles or horses? Their amazing ingenuity came immediately to their aid. They lifted the logs to their shoulders and carried them down into the valley.

Now it happened that a stranger passed by and saw the Chelemites toiling and panting.

"Foolish people," said the stranger, "why do you needlessly puff and sweat?" And having spoken, he

3

pushed one of the logs with his foot and it rolled down the mountain as if it knew exactly where to go.

The builders of Chelem stood and marveled.

"The man is a genius," they whispered to each other.

But Chelemites are quick to learn. Without losing a moment, they went down into the valley, carried the logs back to the summit, and sent them rolling in the precise manner of the stranger.

A CHELEM SOLUTION

The builders of Chelem were digging for the foundation of the synagogue when one of them suddenly dropped his spade and stood still in profound meditation.

"This earth," he muttered to his neighbor who happened to be one of the seven worthies of the town, a man, in other words, of exceptional wisdom.

"Yes, this earth," the worthy repeated and joined his neighbor in contemplation.

"This earth that we are digging up—where are we going to put it?"

The worthy clasped his beard and thought and thought a very long time.

"I have it!" he declared at last. "We'll dig a pit and shovel into it all the earth we are digging up for the foundation of the synagogue!"

His neighbor nodded very slowly.

"But what," he asked, "are we going to do with the earth that we'll dig up from the pit?"

"Nothing is more simple," replied the worthy of Chelem. "We'll dig a second pit, bigger than the first, and shovel its own earth into it as well as the earth of the first pit!"

And the two men of Chelem nodded gravely to each other and resumed their digging.

RIGHT AND LEFT IN CHELEM

The synagogue was duly built, but before long it was observed that the ceiling began to sag.

"We must set up a pillar to support the ceiling," said the wise men of Chelem.

They trimmed a log on top of the mountain for a pillar, but as soon as they brought it to the door of the synagogue a serious question arose and two parties sprang into existence.

"The pillar should be taken in right end first," said one.

"The pillar should be taken in left end first," said the other.

As neither side would yield, the work was brought to a stop and the ceiling was in danger of falling.

Finally one of the seven worthies of the town proposed a compromise which was adopted: to divide the log into two parts and give one to the rightists and the other to the leftists. When this, however, was done, the men of Chelem discovered that each of the parts also had two ends, a right and left. The controversy between the parties broke out afresh.

"Let each of the parts be divided again!" said the

same wise worthy. But when this was done, it was found that each of the ensuing parts had a right and a left, and the controversy became even more acrid.

That day the seven worthies met with the rabbi, and the scribe was ordered to indite the following entry into the Chronicles of Chelem for the remembrance of all generations to come:

"Let all men know by these presents that our eyes have beheld a great truth. A pillar to support the ceiling of a synagogue has always two ends, a right and a left, whether the pillar be entire, or whether it be divided into halves and quarters: and as to whether it should be introduced right end first or left end first, that question we have not been able to resolve: it must stand unanswered until the advent of Elijah the Prophet, may he come speedily and in our days."

A CHELEM COMPROMISE

Now, the public bath-house also presented a grave problem. It had to do with the benches that rose up in tiers almost to the ceiling, on which the bathers stretched out and revelled in the steam and heat. The question was whether the planks for those benches should be smooth or rough.

Immediately two parties came into existence: smoothists and roughists. The smoothists maintained that rough planks would scratch the bodies of the bathers, not to speak of the splinters they would carry home. The roughists argued that smooth planks would make the bathers slip and fall and that some of them might be hurt, *cholileh!*

The wise men of Chelem called a meeting that lasted far into the night. But each party held its ground and the assembly was deadlocked. At last the rabbi proposed a compromise which was universally acclaimed and proved over again that Torah and wisdom go together. His compromise was that the planks should be smooth on one side and rough on the other!

MOVING A MOUNTAIN

The people of Chelem faithfully observed the commandments and in particular the one that ordered all living things including the human species to "be fruitful and multiply." Before long, therefore, the city was overcrowded and it became imperative to extend its area. But a serious obstacle stood in the way of expansion: namely, the mountain at the foot of which the city was built.

The wise men of Chelem met and after much and deep deliberation it was decided to move the mountain. Let skeptics hold their peace: if faith can do it, why not wisdom?

The day for moving the mountain arrived, the men of Chelem flocked to the appointed place, and began by taking off their *kaftans* and piling them together in a heap behind them. Then they rolled up their sleeves and pushed.

Now it happened that a stranger of easy conscience passed by, and seeing the Chelemites engrossed in their labor, he gathered up the *kaftans* and made off with them.

The Chelemites continued to push until they were out of breath and covered with perspiration. They stopped to rest and looking behind them, they observed that their *kaftans* had vanished.

"What does it mean?" they asked each other. "What has become of our *kaftans*?"

Whereupon one of the worthies of the town saw a great light.

"Chelemites!" he cried, "don't you see what has happened? We have moved the mountain so far away, that our *kaftans* are no longer in sight!"

THE RABBI'S WISDOM

As Chelem continued to grow, the people became aware that the place of eternal rest would be insufficient for the population.

"What shall we do?" they asked each other. The cemetery must of course be enlarged, but by how much?

Finally the old rabbi provided the answer. He appointed a day and, at his command, all the inhabitants of Chelem streamed to the cemetery. When they were all there the rabbi stood up and cried.

"Lie down on the ground, every one of you side by side!"

The people obeyed, men, women and children.

"Now measure all around!" said the rabbi to the *shammes.*

"What wisdom!" the Chelemites cried, "What wisdom!"

THE STOLEN MOON

It became known to the people of Chelem that in other cities the streets were lighted at night, and the Chelemites felt that their city must not be behind the times. So a meeting was called, and one of the oldest and wisest of the Chelemites stood up and spoke as follows:

"Let me give you good counsel, my masters. There are nights when the moon shines and Chelem has enough light. There are other nights when there is no moon and Chelem is dark. Why can't the moon shine for us every night? To-morrow night the moon will be at full. Let us go out and capture the moon and keep her for nights that are dark."

The Chelemites approved: wisdom, they declared, lives in old age. Nor had they any difficulty in capturing the moon. They filled a barrel with water, exposed it to the moon, and when that luminary heedlessly entered it, they covered the barrel with sack-cloth held ready for the purpose, and bound it with ropes. In addition, they put the official seal of Chelem on the barrel and brought it into the synagogue.

Some three weeks later the nights began to be dark. The people gathered to take the moon out of the barrel and hang it in the sky. But when they opened the barrel, alas, the moon was gone! They looked at each other ruefully and the wise old man said:

"Somebody has stolen our moon! We should have set watchmen to stand guard over her!"

USES OF A FIRE EXTINGUISHER

It also became known in Chelem that in the big cities it was the practice to put out fires with instruments made for the purpose and called extinguishers. So Chelem, not to be outdone, bought an extinguisher and placed it in the custody of the *shammes*.

The good man soon discovered that the extinguisher might serve as an excellent receptable for things worth preserving, such as clay for sealing up the mouth of the synagogue stove for the summer, horse radish for Passover, garlic for medicinal purposes and many other good things.

Now it happened shortly afterwards that fire broke out in Chelem. At once the extinguisher was brought into play, but the instrument rebelled and refused to open its mouth. The instrument was inspected and found to contain clay, horse radish, garlic, and other things.

The Chelemites were indignant and held a general meeting. A few of the young and reckless came forward and demanded that the *shammes* be deprived of the custody of the extinguisher.

But the older and wiser men demurred.

"No," they said, "the custody of the extinguisher is one of his prerogatives."

Thereupon the others declared:

"Then let the *shammes* swear a solemn oath that henceforth he will not keep in the extinguisher either clay for sealing up the synagogue stove, or horse radish for Passover, or garlic for medicinal purposes, or anything else."

But the older and wiser men demurred again.

"If so, where will the *shammes* put away good things that need to be preserved?"

All day the two parties debated until, at last, they agreed on a compromise as follows:

"The claim of the *shammes* to the custody of the extinguisher is admitted. His right to keep in it all sorts of good things that need to be preserved is also recognized. But he must swear a solemn oath that from now on he will clear everything out of the extinguisher as soon as a fire breaks out in Chelem."

A LADDER TO VIRTUE

It happened once that an abominable thing was done in Chelem: the charity box that stood near the door of the synagogue was stolen! The city was shocked and a meeting was hurriedly called to consider what action should be taken. After prolonged debate it was decided to set up a new charity box and to hang it from the ceiling so that no thief could reach it. Chelem rejoiced: the outrage would never occur again.

But several days later the *shammes* stood before the rabbi.

"The box," said he, "is now beyond the reach of thieves, but it is also beyond the reach of those who might throw in their contributions."

So another meeting was called and a solution to the problem was easily found. A ladder that reached from the floor to the ceiling was set up by which the charitable were able to reach the box. And to make sure that they would not, *cholileh,* be hurt, the ladder was so attached to the floor and ceiling that it could not be moved.

PENOLOGY IN CHELEM

The same assembly deliberated on a question of more general import: what to do with a thief that might be caught redhanded.

The question was referred to the rabbi and the seven worthies of the town who, after deep study, brought in a proposal which was enthusiastically adopted. Two holes, the plan provided, were to be bored in the wall of the bath-house. The culprit was to be brought inside and made to pass his hands through the holes and keep them in that position for as long as the judge should decide. The meaning would be perfectly clear to all the good people of Chelem. It was as though the guilty man himself were to proclaim to all the inhabitants: "Behold! These hands have done the deed!"

In order, however, to make sure that the criminal would not frustrate the plan, it was further provided that rolling pins should be placed in his hands with strict orders to hold them tight.

ARITHMETIC IN CHELEM

The superior mentality for which the Chelemites were famous was not, it should be noted, confined to the men. The women, too, were distinguished for it, as the following tale illustrates.

A stranger once came to Chelem and put up at the tavern. After eating a hearty meal, he asked the mistress of the inn for his account.

"The bread, the soup and the dessert come to seven kopeks," said she. "For the roast, another seven kopeks. Altogether eleven kopeks."

"Pardon me," said her guest, "two times seven are fourteen."

For a moment the woman was puzzled, but only for a moment.

"No," said she. "Two times seven are eleven. I was a widow with four children. I married a widower who also had four children, and three more children were born to us. Now each of us has seven children and altogether we have eleven. Two times seven are eleven."

The stranger paid his account, filled with admiration for the acumen of a mere woman.

A FELINE IN CHELEM

A large animal was once seen prowling through the streets of Chelem and the people were terrified.

Two of the worthies risked their lives for the common good and captured the beast. They made careful inquiry and were informed that the animal was a feline and that its name was "cat."

The same day a solemn meeting was held and it was unanimously decided that the *shammes* should take the beast to the roof of the synagogue and jump down with it to the ground. The *shammes*, of course, would also be killed, but what help was there for it?

The *shammes*, noble man, accepted the verdict, took the animal to the roof and jumped. He died a hero's death, but the cat was seen to run away from under him, alive and well.

Another meeting was called and it was unanimously decided to lock the animal in the synagogue and set fire to the building. The sentence was duly carried out. The synagogue was burnt to the ground, but soon afterwards the beast was seen prowling through the city, alive and well.

The town worthies bowed their heads and recorded the strange event in the Chronicles of Chelem for a memorial to the generations, concluding the entry with the following words:

"To this matter must be applied the verse in Scripture: 'There is no wisdom or understanding or counsel against the will of God.'"

A FISH IN CHELEM

It is well known that not only felines but other creatures of a lower order fail to show proper respect

for their betters. This is well illustrated by what befell Reb Zadok, one of the seven worthies of Chelem.

On a Friday morning, immediately after prayers,
Reb Zadok went to market and bought a live and
handsome fish in honor of the Sabbath. Now, having
to carry his cane in one hand and the bag with his
prayer-shawl and *tefilin* in the other, he slipped the
fish head down into the inside pocket of his *kaftan*
and went his way. But the fish was a big one and the
tail projected out of his pocket.

Suddenly the fish waved his tail and slapped Reb
Zadok full on the face. The fact got around and the
city was in an uproar. Such impudence on the part of
a fish had never been known before!

At once the worthies of Chelem came together and
passed sentence of death upon the culprit. The sentence was carried out immediately. The fish was
taken to the river and drowned.

SNOW IN CHELEM

One Friday afternoon the first snowfall came down
on Chelem and the people rejoiced to see the clean
white blanket covering the rutted streets and dingy
houses of their city. But then they thought sadly:

"The *shammes* will soon be passing through the
town and call on the people to close their shops and
prepare for the Sabbath. What will happen to the
snow when he walks over it?"

Immediately the rabbi and the seven worthies
came together to see what could be done. The snow,

they decided, must at all costs be kept clean. But how will the merchants know when to close their shops for the Sabbath? They might, God forbid, violate the sanctity of the holy day! Finally the rabbi issued an edict as follows:

"The *shammes* is to proclaim the Sabbath as usual. But he is not to go on foot. He is to stand up on a table and be carried through the town by four of the worthies."

A Galaxy of Chelem Worthies

FULL DIRECTIONS

A stranger once came to Chelem and went looking for a man he had come to see. In the course of the quest, the stranger came upon an instance of that passion for exactness which characterized the Chelem mind and of which he had already heard.

"Grandfather," said he, approaching an old man, "can you tell me where Naphtali ben Zemach lives?"

The old man stroked his beard proudly.

"I am a Chelemite," said he, "and my ancestors were Chelemites for ten generations. Is there any one in Chelem I don't know? I know them all, thank God, I know where they live, and I know how they live. You are looking for Naphtali ben Zemach? Do you see that house at the end of the street, the one with two stories? Naphtali ben Zemach does not live there and, as far as I know, he never lived there, neither he nor any of his ancestors. But behind that house there is another one, also of two stories. Go there and climb to the upper story. On that story you will not find the man you are seeking. He never

17

lived there in his life. Go down to the lower story. There you may find him. Naphtali ben Zemach may be living there, but he may never have lived there in his life."

The stranger followed the directions faithfully, but as to whether he found Naphtali ben Zemach the record is silent.

BIG LOAVES AND LITTLE ONES

Later in the day the same stranger discovered the degree to which the reasoning faculty was developed among the people of Chelem.

Having bought a loaf of bread in a bakery, he observed that the loaf was bigger than those that were sold in his own city.

"Why are the loaves in your city bigger than in mine?" he asked the baker.

The baker pondered the question a long time, and at length he found the answer.

"The reason," said he, "must be that in your city the bakers take a smaller piece of dough for each loaf than we do in Chelem."

Filled with admiration, the stranger paid for the loaf and departed.

A PROBLEM IN CONSTRUCTION

The same keen logic stood at the service of a Chelemite who travelled to the capital to buy goods for his shop.

In a restaurant where he happened to be sitting he noticed a big table covered with green cloth. Two individuals armed with long sticks kept striking at some round colored objects that rolled like eggs all over the table.

The strange sight provoked in the mind of the Chelemite a number of puzzling questions.

"Why," he asked himself first, "are they smiting the eggs?"

But that question he promptly dismissed.

"If," he argued, "they find pleasure in it, they will no doubt pay for all the damage they inflict."

The second question was not so simple.

"How," he asked himself, "did they bring the table into the building? It is plain that it could never have gotten through the door."

A long time the Chelemite sat stroking his beard, lost in thought. At length he saw light.

"How do I know," said he, "that they built the house first and brought in the table afterwards? Couldn't they have first brought in the table, then built the house around it?"

A CHELEMITE RECOGNIZED

The same day this Chelemite set out to buy goods for his shop. His name, it should be noted, was Baruch. The day was hot, but he ran from one warehouse to another, panting and perspiring, his cap tilted back on his head, his *kaftan* streaming out behind him. People looked at him in amazement and at length some one stopped him.

"Reb Yankel," said the stranger, "why do you hurry in this heat? Aren't you an idiot?"

"I see," replied the Chelemite, "that you know me. But why did you have to change my name from Baruch to Yankel?"

HE CONSOLES A POOR STRANGER

As Baruch stood on the platform of the station, a train pulled out and the next minute a man came running and stopped, his face full of despair.

"My God!" the man groaned. "My train is gone! What will I do? Everything is lost!"

Reb Baruch was touched and approached the stranger.

"By how much did you miss your train?" he asked him.

"A minute or two," the unhappy man replied.

"Is that all?" said the Chelemite. "Then why do you carry on like that? One would think you had missed it by an hour!"

POOR BUT HONEST

Reb Baruch was glad to be back in Chelem. He had little use for the big city and its ways. His journey made him more certain than ever that the simple and poor were in every way better than the rich. That, of course, was the opinion of all Chelemites, but they asked him if anything had happened in the big city to confirm it.

"Indeed," replied Reb Baruch, "and when I tell you, you will see the difference between the rich and the poor. All day in the big city I ran from one large establishment to another buying goods for my shop. At night I returned to my inn, and behold! I am without my stick! What could I have done with it? I must have forgotten it in one of the big places. Early the following morning I set out to look for my stick. I entered the first place: they denied it. I came to the second: they denied it. I revisited every one of those rich places and every one denied it. At night, tired and broken, I stepped into a small but poor restaurant where I had eaten the night before. Without a word, they produced the stick and returned it to me! There you have the difference between the rich and the poor!"

MERCHANTS IN CHELEM

This tale is one of many that might be cited as evidence of the business acumen for which the Chelemites were famous.

The story is about two of them who agreed to go into partnership and, between them, managed to find enough capital to buy a little keg of whiskey as their stock in trade.

"Berel," said Sholem to his partner, "I have seen many a business like ours ruined by credit. Let us sell for cash only."

"For cash only," Berel agreed.

They opened their business to the public and waited for customers. But no customers came and after a while Berel felt just a little bit discouraged.

"Sholem," said he to his partner, "I have five kopeks in my pocket. Pour me a little glass of whiskey. It's for cash, of course."

Sholem poured and Berel paid and drank. He felt and looked much better.

"Berel," said Sholem to his partner, "I see in your eyes that we have the right stuff. Now that I have five kopeks, I think I'll have a little also. It's for cash, of course."

Berel poured, Sholem paid and drank and he too felt and looked much better.

"Sholem," said Berel to his partner after a rather long pause. "We'll not be so foolish as to sell on credit. Pour me another little glass—for cash, of course."

Berel drank and passed the five kopeks to Sholem. Then Sholem drank again and passed the five kopeks to Berel.

Still there were no customers, but were the partners discouraged? On the contrary! They were in a state of satisfaction bordering on joy!

"Another little glass for me!" said one and paid spot cash.

"Another little glass for me!" said the other and paid spot cash.

The day passed and the contents of the little keg as well. It was time to close up for the day.

"Look, Sholem!" said Berel to his partner, hugging the keg on one side, "In one day we—we sold out our stock—all of it!"

"Yes!" said Sholem, hugging the keg on the other side, "and for—for cash only!"

A LIAR IN CHELEM

The town-liar of Chelem was looking through his window one day, and the urge to lie came strong upon him.

"Listen!" he called down. "There is a cow flying over the roofs behind the bath-house!"

The people heard him and ran. Those who ran told the others and soon the whole town was on its way to see the cow.

The Chelem liar got up, closed his window, and joined the rest.

"Suppose," said he to himself, "there really is a cow flying over the roofs behind the bath-house!"

A LORD AND MASTER IN CHELEM

Connubial relations in Chelem, as is well known, were idyllic. As an instance, take Tanchum the water-carrier and his wife.

Tanchum knew that Holy Writ spoke plainly on the subject. "And he," it says, meaning the husband of course, "shall rule over thee,"* meaning the wife.

Now Tanchum was a big raw-boned man, and

* Genesis, 3, 16.

might have had no difficulty in fulfilling the command, were it not for the fact that his wife, though small and skinny, had sharp features and a still sharper tongue. Her tongue, it was said, was mightier than his brawny hands; and it was even whispered that in moments of abandon she didn't scruple to use her own hands on his face in a manner that pained and confounded him. At such moments, Tanchum the water-carrier had recourse to the nuptial bed, not however in order to lie on it, but in order to take refuge beneath it.

To Tanchum, however, this maneuver meant no surrender of his prerogative. Once, as he lay under the bed, his long legs projecting across the room, a knock was heard upon the door.

"Come out from under the bed and open the door!" said his wife who was standing over him.

"I will not!" Tanchum replied.

"Will you open the door?" she repeated and a grim note sounded in her voice.

But—was Tanchum dismayed?

"No!" he cried from under the bed. "You can't order me around! Who do you think is the master of this house?"

PLUMS IN AND OUT OF THE POT

The wife of Tanchum the water-carrier was really no virago, appearances to the contrary notwithstanding. She was, in fact, a kindly soul. Together with her own children she brought up an orphan boy, the child of a distant relative. The boy was always hungry, nor would it be just to blame the woman, for aren't all growing boys always hungry?

Now one day Tanchum's wife put up a pot of plums on the stove and went away. When she returned the pot was half empty. She didn't have to guess how it happened, and as soon as she was able to lay hands on the boy she let him have it.

The boy raised a loud and bitter outcry, so loud, indeed, that all the neighbors came together and there was much indignation among them.

"To treat a child like that!" cried one.

"And an orphan! Think of it, a poor orphan!" cried another.

"And what is he guilty of?" cried another. "He ate a few plums, the poor child! Was such a thing ever heard of?"

Tanchum's wife listened to the clamor with every appearance of contrition.

"Do you think?" said she finally, "that I begrudge him the few plums he ate? *Cholileh!* But don't you see? Every time he takes one plum and another plum and another, there is less and less in the pot?"

The Chelemites stopped their clamor.

"If that is so," said they, "then, of course, it's different."

A GENTLE SCHOLAR

Or take the case of Reb Pinchas the scholar and his wife. Reb Pinchas spent all his waking hours over the Talmud while the lower needs of the household were provided by the woman. Every morning she set out for the market-place with a big basket of rolls which she baked the night before, and every evening she returned home to prepare food for her scholar. And always, as part of the meal, she saved two of her rolls and placed them beside his plate. Reb Pinchas had a great fondness for his wife's baking.

Now it happened once that the two perpetual rolls were missing!

"Where are the rolls?" asked Reb Pinchas gently.

The good woman answered with tears in her voice. Some drunken soldiers, she told him, passed through the market-place, and made free with her rolls. They emptied the basket and disappeared.

Reb Pinchas was moved by his wife's distress.

"Don't take it so to heart," he told her. "Heaven will repay you."

He sat down to eat. The empty place where the two rolls always lay stared him in the face. A sudden change came over his mood. Reb Pinchas flushed with anger.

"Look now," he cried. "Since they were all taking rolls, why couldn't you have taken two for me?"

TRAGEDY IN CHELEM

It is further on record that the wife of Reb Pinchas once came to the verge of rebellion, demanding that her husband make himself useful in the house at

least. That was the time when a new infant lay in
the cradle and the poor woman needed help.

So one morning before proceeding to the market
place, she gave him definite instructions.

"You are to rock the cradle every time the little
one wakes up, and watch the milk boiling on the
stove that it doesn't run over. I'll be back soon to
nurse him."

Then remembering her scholar's weakness for deli-
cacies, she warned him as follows:

"There is something in a jar in the cupboard. Don't
touch it. It's poison!"

For a while Reb Pinchas pondered on the best
manner of executing his wife's commission; and being
a man of learning and a Chelemite, he contrived a
clever invention. He tied one end of a rope to the
cradle and the other end to his ankle. And taking his
stand near the stove, he was able to rock the cradle
and watch the milk at the same time.

The door opened and in walked a stray dog. There
was a hen in the room tranquilly pecking at the floor.
The hen shrieked, flew over the stove and overturned
the pot of milk. Reb Pinchas snatched at the pot in
an effort to save it and gave the cradle a violent tug.
The cradle overturned and the infant was thrown
out.

Reb Pinchas took in the situation and became desperate. Everything, he realized, had gone wrong.
Everything was lost! Dragging the cradle, he made
his way to the cupboard, found the jar and ate its

contents. Then, still dragging the cradle, he got to the bed, stretched out and waited.

When his wife returned she also took in the situation and burst into tears. She wept and bemoaned her fate, and said harsh things to her husband.

"*Gazlon*," said she finally, "why are you stretched out on the bed?"

"I have eaten the poison in the jar," said Reb Pinchas, "and I am waiting for death."

THE LOST NOTEBOOK

Chelem had a *maggid* who once suffered a serious loss. The *maggid* went out to preach in a nearby town. On the road he was overtaken by a peasant's wagon piled high with fodder.

"May I ride with you?" said he to the driver.

The peasant agreed, and the *maggid* climbed up and made himself comfortable in the fodder. He fell asleep and slept until he came to his destination.

The *maggid* stopped in the inn, and began to prepare his sermon. He looked for the little notebook in which he kept his themes and parables, but alas, the notebook was gone! Again and again he rummaged through his clothes but the precious memorandum failed to turn up.

"I lost it in the fodder!" said the *maggid* to himself. "Now some horse, or ass, or cow will eat it and get to know all my sermons!"

And the *maggid* of Chelem hastened to the synagogue, ascended the Bimah and smote the table for silence.

"My masters!" he proclaimed, "I solemnly declare that if some horse, or ass, or cow should come to this town to preach, the sermons will be mine and not theirs!"

The Rabbi of Chelem

EAST AND WEST

Concerning the rabbi of Chelem many tales have come down, all tending to show how perfectly he and his people were suited to each other. He was a saint, gentle, kind, and, of course, wise, a genuine Chelemite. At the same time he frowned on over-clever people as the following story proves.

The rabbi was once summoned to perform the marriage ritual, and when he reached the courtyard of the synagogue where the ceremony was to take place, he found the couple under the canopy facing west. The rabbi objected:

"It is a custom in Israel for the bride and groom to stand under the canopy facing east," said he.

The *shammes* came forward and turned the canopy around. But the couple still faced west. The younger men of Chelem took counsel together and changed the position of the poles. But that too proved useless: the couple still faced west.

But a stranger chanced to be present in the synagogue courtyard, and some believe that he was a

Litvak. He approached the couple, turned them around without ceremony and at once they faced east. The rabbi of Chelem was amazed.

"Where did you learn that?" he asked.

"That is how we do it in my city," replied the stranger.

The rabbi shook his head.

"Yes," he said, "apparently there are no people like those in your city for being smart and unmannerly."

NOT A TRUE SIGN

One day the news spread through Chelem that the body of a slain man had been discovered within the precincts of the city. Chelem was in a state of panic, but when the rabbi issued a call for all the people to gather in order to identify the victim, they all came.

As all of them, men, women and children, stood gazing upon the corpse, a woman suddenly clapped her hands and shrieked:

"Woe is me! It's my husband!"

Said the rabbi to her:

"Daughter, have you a sure sign for identification?"

The woman sobbed and said:

"Yes, rabbi, I have a true sign: my husband was a stammerer."

"It's a sure sign, a sure sign!" the Chelemites agreed.

But the old rabbi shook his head in dissent.

"You are mistaken, my daughter," said he to the

poor woman, "that is not a sure sign. There are many stammerers in the world."

WHY NOT?

In other matters, too, the rabbi's knowledge was vast, while with respect to domestic animals his ideas were distinctly original. Consider, for example, the following incident:

A wagoner and a horse dealer once came to the rabbi with a serious dispute. Said the wagoner:

"This man is a swindler. I bought a horse from him and paid for it, and when I took the animal home, it bit the manger and broke its teeth. That's the kind of horse he sold me."

And the horse dealer said:

"As long as I had that horse he never bit the manger."

Finally the rabbi said:

"This is a hard case and requires a great deal of study. Come back to-morrow."

And when they returned, the rabbi said to the wagoner:

"All night I studied your case and I find the law is not on your side. What compels you to place the manger at the horse's head? Why not at his tail?"

STRANGE WAYS OF A CALF

Or take the remarkable feat of the old rabbi with his calf. When the calf was born the pious man gazed with wonder upon the creature.

"How marvellous are the ways of Heaven!" said he: "A human being is born with only two legs but is unable to use them until a long time afterwards. This creature is born with four legs and is at once able to use them for standing and walking."

And some days later the rabbi found the calf lying in his yard asleep. He walked around it with great curiosity, and was finally taken with a desire to test the animal's strength. He seized the calf's tail and pulled it. The calf woke up frightened, and rushed out of the yard into the street, the rabbi clinging to its tail with both hands and all his strength, but unable to check it.

Realizing his desperate situation the rabbi cried aloud:

"Good people, quick, cut off the creature's tail, or it will kill me!"

AN IMPARTIAL JUDGE

What is most important in the character of a judge? All will admit that impartiality is most important. The impartiality of the rabbi of Chelem was famous for miles around.

Two litigants came to him one day to settle their dispute. After listening long and patiently to the plaintiff, he said to him:

"You are in the right."

Then he listened to the defendant and said to him:

"You are in the right."

The litigants departed highly pleased, but the

rabbi's wife, who was present, was puzzled. A mere woman, what would she understand of legal matters?

"How is it possible," said she, "that they should both be in the right?"

The rabbi pondered the question long and deeply. Finally he turned to his good wife and said:

"Shall I tell you something? You are also in the right."

CERTIFICATE OF FRIENDSHIP

But it appears that the strict impartiality for which the rabbi of Chelem was noted had the effect of reducing the number of those who came to him to judge their cases. The rabbi's livelihood began to dwindle.

"We'll starve," said his wife one day. "Nobody comes here any more."

"The reason," said the rabbi, "is that the people of Chelem, God bless them, are not litigious as people in other places are."

Nevertheless he used to stand at his window and look out for possible litigants. And once he saw two men approaching who seemed to be engaged in sharp dispute. They waved their arms in violent gestures and spoke at the top of their voices. The rabbi opened his window and called them in.

"Let me adjudicate your dispute," he said to them.

"But, rabbi," they told him, "we have no dispute! We were just engaged in a friendly conversation!"

"In that case," said the rabbi, "let me give you a certificate that you have nothing against each other."

The Chelemites accepted the certificate and went away highly pleased.

THE RABBI AND HIS HEAD

One day, the news spread like wildfire through Chelem that the rabbi had vanished! A dreadful foreboding fell upon the town. Everybody, young and old, great and small, went out to look for him. They ranged through the forest, they searched in caves and in wells. At last they found something. They found a headless corpse!

The good people of Chelem were shocked, but at the same time they were puzzled. They were not sure it was the rabbi: they did not remember whether or not their rabbi had a head.

So they called for the *shammes* and asked him if the rabbi had a head.

The *shammes* pondered a long time.

"I know," said he, "that he had a beard, because he put away between the leaves of his Talmud every hair that fell from his beard. But as for a head, I don't know."

So they sent for the keeper of the bath-house.

"Did the rabbi have a head?" they asked him.

The keeper of the bath-house pondered a long time.

"I know," said he, "that the rabbi had earlocks, because on the day before every Sabbath and festival he washed his earlocks in hot water which I brought him. But whether or not he had a head, I cannot say."

So they sent a deputation to the rabbi's wife.

"Did the rabbi have a head?" they asked her.

A long time the good woman was silent.

"I know," said she finally, "that the rabbi had a nose because I prepared him a supply of snuff for every Sabbath and festival. But whether or not he had a head, I cannot say."

And did the rabbi of Chelem have a head? To this day nobody knows.

A Melamed in Chelem

THE *MELAMED* OF CHELEM

Now with regard to the *melamed* of Chelem it
goes without saying that he was in every respect a
true Chelemite. How could it be otherwise? Isn't
every genuine *melamed,* no matter where he may
live and labor, a Chelemite?

The *melamed* of Chelem was particularly shrewd
in matters economic and financial.

"You know," said he to his wife one day, "if I were
the Czar, I would be richer than the Czar."

"How so?" she asked.

"I would do a little teaching on the side," he explained.

MONEY AND CREDIT

With regard to money, the *melamed* of Chelem
had his feet on the ground. He had no patience with
people who exaggerate.

"More than once," he used to say, "I have had as
much as three rubles all my own at the end of a

semester. My father-in-law had four rubles when I married his daughter. Once I saw with my own eyes thirty-five rubles in the hand of the richest man in Chelem. But when people come and tell you they saw a hundred rubles, they either lie, or else they are the victims of hallucination, God shield us!"

And once as he sat thinking on the strange ways of the world, he arrived at a new solution of the problem of credit.

"It's a topsy-turvy world," he declared to his wife. "The rich who have plenty of money buy on credit. The poor, who haven't a copper, have to pay cash. Isn't it common sense it should be the other way: the rich to pay cash and the poor to get credit? What's that you say? A merchant who gives credit to the poor will become a poor man himself? Very well! What if he does? He'll be able to buy on credit, won't he?"

AN HONEST ANSWER

There was a foolish scoffer in Chelem who once tried to embarrass the *melamed* on the question of money.

"*Melamed*," said he, "if you found a million rubles in the market-place, would you yield to the temptation to keep the money or would you return it to its owner?"

The *melamed* answered without hesitation.

"If I knew," said he, "that the money belonged to Rothschild, I fear I would not be able to overcome the temptation. If, however, I knew that the money belonged to someone like the Chelemer *Shammes*, I would certainly return it!"

CLASS DISTINCTIONS

The *melamed* of Chelem laid no claim to a knowledge of the latest pedagogic methods, nevertheless he had his own way of impressing his teachings on his pupils. Consider, for example, the following discourse he once held to acquaint his pupils with the differences that exist among the social classes.

"An ordinary man," said the *melamed*, "puts on a clean shirt on Friday for the Sabbath. A rich man changes his shirt every day. Rothschild changes his shirt three times a day, in the morning, at noon, and in the evening. The Czar is attended by two generals, one of whom takes off the shirt he wears and the other puts on a clean one, off and on, off and on, without interruption, night and day.

"An ordinary man takes a nap and who takes care he should not be awakened? His wife. A rich man is protected by a vestibule before his sleeping room. Rothschild has twelve men stationed before his bedroom to guard his sleep. The Czar has an army of soldiers before his door, who cry continually and all together: 'Quiet! His Majesty is sleeping!'

"An ordinary man gets up early in the morning and eats his breakfast. A rich man sleeps till ten o'clock, then he gets up and has his breakfast. Rothschild sleeps until Afternoon Prayers, and eats his breakfast towards evening. The Czar sleeps all day and all night, and has his breakfast the following day."

BIRTH CONTROL

Early in his career, the *melamed* of Chelem obtained a charge in a neighboring town and although the place was not far distant, he returned to his family only once a year, on the occasion of the Holy Days.

"You are so near," said the rabbi to him, "why don't you come in every week for the Sabbath?"

"I come in once a year," the *melamed* explained, "and every year my wife has a baby. If I came in for every Sabbath, she might, *cholileh,* have a baby every week."

MY SLIPPERS, YOUR SLIPPERS

And once it happened that returning to his charge, the *melamed* forgot his slippers; and when he learned that one of the villagers was leaving for the town, he gave him a letter for his wife as follows:

"Be sure to send me your slippers with this messenger. I have put down 'your slippers,' because if I wrote 'my slippers' you would read my slippers, and would send me your slippers. And what would I do with your slippers? Therefore, I say plainly 'your slippers' so that you would read your slippers and send me my slippers."

THE *MELAMED* AND HIS WIFE

The *melamed* of Chelem and his wife had lived together for many years, a model of harmony and concord. In their old age, however, a deplorable event occurred which broke the even tenor of their common life. But since there is nothing wholly good or wholly evil, the same event led to the enactment of an ordinance which brought lasting benefit to Chelem. The event as well as the ordinance must now be recorded.

It all began with an innocent conversation between the *melamed* and his wife. It was in the evening when his labors were over and the good woman was knitting a stocking.

"Rifkele," said the *melamed*. "Here am I nearly seventy years old and never have I eaten a cake stuffed with cheese and kneaded with butter. And the holy festival of Shevuos is at hand, when it is a great *mitzvah* to partake of such pastry."

The woman stopped her knitting, her eyes became wistful and her mouth watered. She sighed and said:

"Alas! I can say the same for myself."

For a long time the *melamed* stroked his beard lost in thought.

"I have a good idea," said he at length. "Do you remember the big trunk you brought as part of your dowry? We haven't used it all these years. Let us cut two openings in the cover, and every day I'll throw a little coin out of my earnings into one and you'll throw a little coin out of your allowance into the other. The day before Shevuos we'll open the trunk and there will be enough for flour and eggs and cream and cheese. We'll have a cake befitting the holy festival."

"So be it," the good woman replied.

But in his heart the *melamed* thought deceitfully.

"How is it possible," said he to himself, "for me to spare anything from my wretched earnings? Let her deposit her mite and it will be enough."

But in her heart she too thought deceitfully.

"It's impossible for me to spare anything," said she to herself. "He will throw in his coins and they will suffice."

At last came the spring and the lovely festival of Shevuos. With beating hearts the *melamed* and his wife unlocked the trunk, lifted the cover and looked in. The trunk was empty!

The good woman flew into a rage.

"Where are your coins?" she screamed and dug her hands into his beard.

The *melamed* was outraged.

"Woman of evil, where are your coins?" he thundered and buried his hands into her wig.

And as they struggled back and forth they both fell into the trunk. The cover came down with a crash, and the lock snapped shut.

Now, the trunk, it must be told, was very big and, to move it more easily, it was furnished with four wheels, one in each corner. Moreover, the day being warm, the door of the house was ajar and—a cir-

cumstance of grave importance—the doorway had
no threshold. And because the *melamed* and his wife,
both transported with rage, still struggled within it,
the trunk began to move. It made for the open door,
and, with no threshold to arrest its progress, it rolled
out into the street.

On the same street stood the synagogue. The trunk
continued its journey and came to a halt inside the
holy place.

People saw the trunk rolling solitary down the
street, but no one dared touch it, so astonished were
they all and terrified by the sight. And when finally
they saw it inside the house of worship, skipping,
veering, and pitching, and heard muffled sounds,
strange and unearthly, issue from its entrails, they
were seized with panic and ran to the rabbi and the
seven worthies.

The rabbi and the worthies of Chelem came together and took immediate action. They adopted a
solemn resolution that, for the sake of the common
weal, the *shammes* must risk his life and open the
trunk. The *shammes*, noble man, accepted the charge.
He performed special ablutions, prayed devoutly and
put on his burial robes. Then he entered the synagogue, opened the trunk and found the *melamed*
and his wife clasped in desperate struggle, her hands
still in his beard and his in her wig.

Again the rabbi and the seven worthies came together and spent a long time in profound deliberation. The outcome was an ordinance in four sections

which brought untold benefit to the town of Chelem for all time:

One: Every door in Chelem must have a threshold.

Two: A *melamed* must not live on the street where the synagogue stands.

Three: It is not seemly for an old *melamed*, whose wife knits stockings, to hanker after Shevuos pastry.

Four: A trunk that is brought as part of a dowry must not be furnished with wheels.

HE-GOAT, SHE-GOAT

The tale must now be told of the strange transformations that befell the *melamed* of Chelem and of the wise men who by their insight into the mysteries of nature, found the answer to a baffling riddle.

"A goat," said the *melamed's* wife one day, "is a blessing in a household. A good goat," she continued, "is no trouble or expense to her owner; she finds her own food and gives milk in abundance."

Nor did Rifkele, the *melamed's* wife, intend her words to be merely general. It was the end of the semester and she knew her husband to have some money hidden away somewhere.

"Go," said she to him, "to the neighboring town, which is famous in the land for its goats. Go and bring home a good goat."

"A foolish woman," said the *melamed* to himself, "but this time she is right. There is merit in a good goat."

So he went to the town of goats, bought a good

goat, and the same day set out with his goat for Chelem. Here and there on the way the goat stopped to browse and, although it was late, the *melamed* did nothing to prevent her. His heart went out to the gentle beast.

But twilight and darkness fell upon the earth and the *melamed* feared to continue lest robbers overtake him and steal his goat. So he stepped aside into an inn, tied the goat in the shed of the courtyard and asked the innkeeper for a bed for the night.

Now the innkeeper was a garrulous and frivolous person, having no decent respect for Chelemites in general and for a *melamed* of Chelem in particular. So, the *melamed* having retired for the night, the man went to the shed, untied the goat, and put a he-goat in her place.

The following morning the *melamed* resumed his journey and arrived home in triumph.

"Rifkele," he cried, "I have brought you a goat, such a year on all good and pious people. Take your pail and milk her."

But when the woman discovered what sort of a goat her *melamed* had brought her, she turned pale with anger and called down a series of strange curses impartially upon the head of the goat and that of her husband. The *melamed* listened to her meekly, but when she included his immediate ancestors in her maledictions, he roused himself and resolved to return forthwith to the man who had sold him the goat, and demand satisfaction.

Without a moment's delay, the *melamed* seized

the rope that was tied to the horns of the goat and set out. He travelled at a rapid pace and when he came to the inn he thought to rest a bit, and having tied the goat in the shed, he told the innkeeper of the unheard of betrayal that had been practised upon him. The innkeeper bided his time and at the right moment proceeded to the shed, released the he-goat, and tied the she-goat in his place.

The *melamed* came to the goat-merchant and stood before him with all the dignity of injured innocence.

"How does a man permit himself," he demanded more in sorrow than in wrath, "to sell a *melamed* a he-goat instead of a she-goat?"

The merchant looked at the goat and laughed.

"*Melamed!*" he cried, as if the appellation connoted ridicule, instead of honor, "can't you see it's a she-goat?"

And he called his wife, who brought a pail, and in the presence of the astonished *melamed*, milked the goat until the pail brimmed over.

The *melamed*, bewildered and crestfallen, took the goat and set out for Chelem. He spent the night in the same inn, and when he returned to his wife the following morning he brought her a he-goat instead of a she-goat. The unsuspecting woman attempted to milk the creature, her face became purple with rage, and she called down a dreadful curse upon the *melamed's* ancestors to the tenth generation. And when the *melamed* heard it he was seized with terror, and grasping the rope that was tied to the goat's horns, he set out immediately to confront the merchant with the clear evidence of his duplicity. On the way he stopped to rest in the inn, and when he stood before the merchant the animal he led by the rope was not a he-goat but a she-goat. The merchant again laughed at the *melamed*, called his wife who again milked the beast, filling her pail to the brim.

The *melamed* refused to believe his eyes.

"Impossible!" he cried. "I will not believe it unless the rabbi and the magistrates attest in a written document that this animal is a she-goat and not a he-goat."

So the rabbi and the magistrates came together, and after a thorough examination, they drew up a document which was witnessed by the seven elders and sealed with the seal of the congregation, that the animal was a she-goat in every particular.

The *melamed* took the document and the goat and set out for Chelem. On the way he stopped to rest in the same inn and when he arrived home he brought his wife a he-goat.

The woman, after innocently trying to milk it, sat down and wept. The *melamed*, dazed and desperate, took out the document and waved it.

"The animal is a she-goat!" he shouted. "Here is a document that proves it!"

The noise brought the people of Chelem to the *melamed's* door. They swarmed about the place and presently two parties rose up among them.

"The woman is right," declared one party. "The animal is a he-goat. The signs are unmistakable."

"The *melamed* is right," maintained the other, "the

animal is a she-goat. The document is not to be denied."

Finally the *melamed*, his wife and the goat, followed by all the people of Chelem, proceeded to the rabbi of the town and laid the matter before him. The rabbi listened carefully, put on his spectacles, examined the animal thoroughly, read the document again and again and at length pronounced his verdict.

"The law," he declared, "is on the side of the *melamed*. The animal is a she-goat and the document establishes this fact beyond all doubt. But it is equally clear, and it must be ordained from on high, that the moment a she-goat is brought into Chelem, she becomes transformed into a he-goat."

And the good people of Chelem, the *melamed* and his wife included, acknowledged the wisdom of the verdict and went home in peace.

L'ENVOI FOR THE *MELAMED*

Once the *melamed* of Chelem was discovered by an acquaintance at a fair in a neighboring town.

"*Melamed*," said the acquaintance, "what business have you at the fair?"

"I came," the *melamed* replied, "because I had an idea I would find a driver who would give me a lift back to Chelem."

Tanchum the Water Carrier

TANCHUM GOES TO MARKET

For a proper understanding of Chelem, it may be instructive to consider the career of one of its undistinguished citizens, say, Tanchum the water carrier, of whom something has already been told. For even the ordinary Chelemite is not to be ignored.

The Chelem in Tanchum came out early in life. His mother once sent him to market to buy a chicken and he came back with a pitcher of water!

"Woe is me!" cried his mother. "Where is the chicken?"

"I went to the woman who sells chickens," Tanchum explained. "The woman said her chickens were wonderful; they were so fat. 'Oho!' said I, 'fat is better than chickens!' I went to the butcher to buy fat. The butcher said his fat was wonderful; it was like oil. 'Oho!' said I, 'oil is better than fat!' I went to the grocer to buy oil. The grocer said his oil was wonderful; it was as pure as water. 'Oho' said I. 'Water is better than oil!' So here I am with a pitcher of water!"

HE TRIES THE MATCHES

On another occasion his mother sent him to buy matches.

"Be sure to try them," she warned him; "make sure they light."

Tanchum came back with the matches and his mother tried them. She tried one, two, three; they refused to light.

"Didn't I tell you to try them before you buy them?" she cried.

"I did," said Tanchum, "I tried them all. They were all good."

HE HAS HIS PRIDE

Even when he was still young Tanchum was noted for his pride. His mother found him in the kitchen one day, and the dog was standing over a bowl of milk lapping it up.

"Tanchum!" she cried. "Why don't you chase the dog away?"

"I don't talk to him," Tanchum explained. "He ripped my pants yesterday."

HIS CAREER AS SHOEMAKER

For a number of years, Tanchum *Tippesh* was a shoemaker, and this is his own account of it.

"My father and mother were at odds," he explained.

"She wanted me to be a tailor and he wanted me to be a shoemaker. In the end he had his way. And let me tell you, it was fortunate for me that he did, for otherwise I would be starving. I have been following my trade now for four years and it hasn't happened yet that anyone who comes to me should order clothes. They all order shoes!"

HE GOES TO TOWN

In a spirit of enterprise Tanchum made his way to the big city and strange as it may sound, he tried his hand at business. Out of his brief career in that field, the following incident is remembered:

His employer once sent him to a neighboring town to collect from a customer whose account was in arrears.

"Tanchum," said his employer before sending him off, "when you get to the town go about your business very subtly. Begin by visiting the market place. Step into a restaurant and order a cup of coffee. Look around, start a conversation with your neighbor. Inquire casually about our customer. Find out if he is still solvent. Then drop in on him, be courteous but firm, and try to collect as much as possible. As soon as you know definitely how much he is ready to pay, send me a telegram."

The following day, Tanchum sent his employer a telegram as follows:

"No coffee in this town. What shall I do?"

HE GETS SLAPPED

When the train on which Tanchum returned pulled into the station, a tall person was seen striding up and down the platform and calling, "Yeruchem! Yeruchem!"

Tanchum put his head out of the window and looked inquiringly at the tall person. The latter ran forward and slapped Tanchum twice in the face.

The other passengers laughed and Tanchum also laughed.

"Why are you laughing?" they asked him. "You are the one who got slapped."

"Yes," said Tanchum, "but my name isn't Yeruchem, it's Tanchum!"

HE FINDS HIS TRUE VOCATION

In the big city Tanchum took a wife—things like that always happen. Soon Tanchum returned to Chelem with his wife and he became a water carrier.

Tanchum was satisfied with his lot and happy. Sometimes his work brought him unexpected pleasures. Once when he went down to the river to fill his pails, he saw his wife on the bank downstream washing his clothes. On a flat stone before her lay his drawers, and she was beating them with a heavy wooden implement. Tanchum watched the operation and a wave of gratitude swept over him. There and then he made up a new blessing.

"Blessed art thou, O Lord," said he, "who gavest me understanding to get out of my drawers in time."

HE TRIUMPHS OVER HIS WIFE

Tanchum's wife, it must be confessed, was not so easily satisfied. It mustn't be forgotten that she came from the big city. After living in certain quarters for ten years, she insisted on moving to better ones.

What did Tanchum do? He yielded. Is it possible to make head against a wife who always tells you about the luxury she enjoyed before she was married?

She went out and found new quarters. Shortly after they installed themselves, a fire broke out in the neighborhood. Tanchum and his wife stood at the window and looked out. The next minute they saw the house next to theirs in flames.

"Do you see?" said Tanchum to his wife gleefully, "you always tell me that I am a *tippesh*. But who was it that rented a place right next to a burning house? Was it you or I?"

HE TRIUMPHS AGAIN

In her heart of hearts, Tanchum's wife was fond of him, but she was also ashamed of him. "You're such a *tippesh*," she used to say to him. Moreover, she began to hanker for the big city. That's how they are, the women who come from the grand places!

She decided to get a divorce and took him to the rabbi.

"What have you against him?" asked the rabbi.

"He's a *tippesh*," she answered.

"How long have you lived together?" asked the rabbi.

"Fifteen years."

"Fifteen years and you've only now discovered that he is a *tippesh*?"

At this point Tanchum could no longer contain himself.

"She is not telling the truth, rabbi," he cried. "She has known it all along!"

The rabbi of Chelem refused to divorce them and they lived happily ever afterwards.

Wagoner and Brigand

A SIMPLE WAGONER BECOMES A BRIGAND

The Chelem *baal-agalah* was a good and pious soul, though not among the wisest of his townsmen. But, being a Chelemite, he could not altogether escape the effects of that wisdom with which the very air of the town was impregnated. Consider, for example, the following bit which has been recorded as having dropped from his lips:

"Blessed be the Holy One," said the wagoner, "who ordained the Sabbath for His people Israel! Without the day of rest a hard-working man like me would go under. It's only a pity that He didn't establish the Sabbath for the middle of the week. At the end of the week I am too tired to enjoy it properly."

But the Chelemites were not given to travelling and the wagoner's business was never in a flourishing state. Why, indeed, should Chelemites go gadding about? Did other cities have anything to teach them?

It happened that the poor *baal-agalah* came to the end of his resources. He even tried other callings, but with no better success. So, in desperation, he decided to become a brigand.

He found his opportunity and slipped the kitchen knife into his pocket. Then he made off for the forest where he sat down beside a road and waited. He waited a long time and the sun began to set.

"Time for *Minchah*," said he to himself.

He chanted the "Happy Are They," then faced east and began the Eighteen Benedictions. He was only half through when some one came up the road. The wagoner signalled to the man to wait, for, as everybody knows, the Eighteen Benedictions cannot be interrupted for anyone or anything. The man waited.

The wagoner ended the Benedictions, went three steps backward as the ritual requires, and chanted the "*Aleinu*," which closes the Afternoon Prayer. And then, without losing a moment, he approached the man and seized him by the lapels of his coat.

"Money or your life!" he cried.

The man was dumbfounded.

"Have you gone crazy?" he cried, for he knew the wagoner very well.

But the brigand knew no pity.

"I am not crazy," he shouted. "I am a *gazlon*, do you understand?"

And with that he whipped the knife out of his pocket and brandished it over the head of his victim.

But suddenly the wagoner lowered his hand and turned pale.

"My God," he moaned, "I took the *milchige* knife instead of the *fleishige*."*

* The dietary laws require different utensils for "milk" dishes and "meat" dishes.

The wagoner took to his heels and disappeared in the forest. He spent the night beneath the stars and decided to try again on the morrow. The knife, he realized, was useless, but he would have recourse to another method, the simple method of intimidation.

The day happened to be "Lag B'Omer," the only day in the seven weeks that follow Passover when festivities are not forbidden. On that day it is customary for teachers and pupils to go to the woods for an outing.

And sure enough, as the *gazlon* trudged through the woods he came upon a group of jolly, shouting children and their *melamed*.

The *baal-agalah* burst upon the scene and shouted, "Hands up!"

Every pair of hands shot up into the air, except the *melamed's*.

The *gazlon* turned fiercely upon the poor man.

"Hands up, *melamed!*" he thundered. "I'm a brigand, can't you see?"

"I—I can't lift my hands," the *melamed* stammered. "I have a terrible pain in my shoulder!"

"A pain in your shoulder?" exclaimed the *gazlon*. "Ay, ay, ay! Have you tried iodine? Sometimes hot compresses are very good. Try them, try them!"

And the *gazlon* disappeared.

He went his way deeper into the forest and before long the sound of footsteps reached his ear. He stepped aside, and when the wayfarer came in sight, he barred his way.

"Money or your life!" he cried.

"What?" said the man. "Do I look like Rothschild to you? I'm a pauper. I beg for alms from door to door. What can I give you?"

"Well," said the brigand more quietly, "it doesn't have to be much. A small coin will do, say ten kopeks."

"Ten kopeks! I have to knock on thirty doors before I collect so much."

"Well then, can you spare a cigarette? I haven't smoked all day."

"But I don't smoke!"

"Oh! It's too bad. In that case, give me a pinch of snuff. There is nothing like a good pinch of snuff to set a man up!"

The wayfarer took out his snuff-box, opened and extended it to the brigand, who helped himself to a large pinch. He inhaled the snuff and sneezed three times in quick succession.

"Good health to you and long life!" said the stranger.

"Long life and good health to you!" replied the brigand.

And the two shook hands and went their separate ways.

And after that the *baal-agalah* returned to his wife and children and to his horse and wagon.

CAN'T MOVE, CAN'T STOP

When after many years, the railroad at Chelem was completed, the event created a vast sensation. People stood at the station to see the first train depart.

"Now we shall see the big wagons ride without horses," said they.

The old *baal-agalah* of Chelem was still incredulous.

"Impossible," said he, "wagons don't move without horses."

A shrill whistle was heard, but the train stood still.

"Whistle away!" said the wagoner, "but if you want to move you'll have to get horses."

Again the whistle sounded, but the train didn't stir.

"What did I tell you?" said the wagoner in triumph. "I ought to know something about it. I've been a wagoner for fifty years!"

The whistle sounded a third time and, wonder of wonders! The wheels began to grind, the big wagons began to move, and the train bounded away.

A moment the wagoner was dumb with amazement; then he recovered.

"How are you going to stop it?" he cried. "It will never stop! Never!"

Chelem Philosophers

THE WISE AMONG THE WISE

It is a known fact that there are degrees of wisdom as there are degrees of piety, humility, benevolence, and all other virtues. The wise men of Chelem were not all equally wise. There were some among them who were supremely wise: philosophers, thinkers, illuminated spirits. Who was as wise as Lemach ben Lekish, for example? Or as his friend and almost his namesake, Lekish ben Lemach? These two were the center of a group, a school, a cénacle, who held meetings every Sabbath afternoon in the synagogue, and delved into the secrets of nature, the mysteries of life, the problems of society, and other questions that baffle lesser minds.

THE WISDOM OF LEMACH BEN LEKISH

No one disputed Lemach's pre-eminence among the philosophers of Chelem. No question was too deep for him. Take the following as mere illustrations:

"Why," he was asked, "does a dog wag his tail?"

"Because," Lemach answered without hesitation, "the dog is stronger than the tail. Were it the other way, the tail would wag the dog."

Again he was asked why the hair on a man's head turns gray sooner than his beard.

"It's because," Lemach replied, "the hair on his head is twenty years older than his beard."

"And why," he was further asked, "are the waters of the seas salty?"

"Don't you know?" he said. "It's because of the thousands of herring that live there."

CHELEM FOUND SAFE

A stranger once came to Chelem and reported that the river that flowed through his city had overrun its banks and flooded half the town. When the Chelemites heard this they feared for their own city. What if they too should be flooded? So great was the anxiety in Chelem that some of the people lost all desire for food.

"There is no ground for fear!" declared Lemach ben Lekish. "Chelem is safe!"

"How do you know?" asked the stranger.

"We have no river in Chelem," said Lemach, "we have a lake."

"But a lake may also overflow its shores," said the stranger.

"Not ours," Lemach answered him. "We have so many fish in our lake that they drink up all the excess water."

And with that the anxiety that weighed on Chelem was lifted.

GROWTH OF MAN

The philosopher Lekish ben Lemach, on the other hand, had a way of startling his fellow-thinkers with unexpected questions.

"From which of his extremities does a man grow?" he once asked them. "From his feet down or from his head up?"

After a long and deep silence one of them ventured a reply.

"I remember," said he, "when I was a boy my father bought me a pair of trousers. When I first put them on they dragged on the floor. Two years later they only reached to my ankles. That proves that a man grows from his feet down."

"Not so," Lekish replied, "I was in the market-place yesterday and a company of soldiers marched through. I looked carefully and saw that their feet were all on a level, but their heads were not. Some heads came high, others were low, and it became clear to me that a man grows from his head up."

And the wise men of Chelem nodded in agreement.

BIRDS AND COWS

It is related that one day Lemach ben Lekish and Lekish ben Lemach were strolling outside the town of Chelem discoursing on the wonders of creation. It was a pleasant day in summer; above them the birds darted and twittered, and the cows grazed lazily in the meadows.

One of the philosophers stopped and became lost in thought.

"The ways of Heaven are mysterious," said he finally. "Consider the birds and the cows. The bird is small and his needs are modest. Nevertheless he has been given wings and he has access to the sky as well as the earth. The cow is big and her needs are much greater. Nevertheless she is held down to the earth alone."

Now, as the speaker looked up towards the sky, a flock of birds flew by and something fell on his nose. Hastily he turned aside and wiped his face with his sleeve.

"What is it?" asked his companion.

"I have found the solution to the mystery!" declared the other joyfully.

"Indeed! What have you found?" asked the other thinker.

"I have been shown the reason why the Lord in His wisdom and mercy thought it best not to give wings to the cow."

BUTTER DOWN, BUTTER UP

The two philosophers met one day and a single glance at his friend's countenance revealed to Lemach that Lekish was deeply disturbed.

"Tell me what it is that weighs on your mind," said Lemach.

"Lemach," said Lekish, "is it not an established fact that whenever a poor màn, like you or me, drops his bread it always falls butter-side down?"

"It is so indeed," Lemach replied.

"This morning," Lekish continued, "I dropped my bread and it fell butter-side up."

"Ah!" Lemach exclaimed, as he realized fully the strangeness of the event.

"All day," Lekish continued, "I have thought about it, and I am unable to explain it."

"Mmm!" Lemach mused as his intellect began to grapple with the problem. But he struggled in vain. Sunk in silent meditation, the two sat together a long time and when darkness fell they separated and sighed deeply as they bade each other good night.

At a small hour of the morning, Lekish was awakened by a gentle knocking on his window. He opened the door and Lemach stood on the threshold in the moonlight.

"I have the explanation!" Lemach whispered. "It's because you buttered your bread on the wrong side!"

And the two philosophers, clad in their night-robes, embraced ecstatically beneath the moon.

WHAT A SPLASH!

It was noted once that for several days Lemach ben Lekish, the dean of the Chelem philosophers, failed to appear among his companions. When they inquired about him they were alarmed to learn that Lemach was refusing food and drink and spending his nights without sleep or rest. Lemach, they knew, was in the throes of some profound speculation.

So they came to him and begged him to unburden himself to them.

"Perhaps," said they, "this will bring you relief."

For a long time Lemach made no answer, but finally, when they implored him again and again, he yielded.

"This," said he, "is the thought that torments me. If all men now on the face of the earth became one man; if all the trees in all the forests became one tree; if all the seas on the earth became one ocean; if all the axes in the world became one ax; and the man arose and took the ax, and cut down the tree and it fell into the ocean—"

Lemach halted and his listeners drew a deep breath.

"Then what? Then what?" they whispered.

"Then, then," Lemach whispered in reply, "how loud would that splash be?"

HORSES AND OXEN

Many difficult questions have been solved by the philosophers of Chelem by what may be called collective thinking, one of them asking, another answering.

"Everybody knows," said one of them once, "that oxen are killed for meat and horses are not. Nevertheless, there are always more oxen than horses. How does that happen?"

"It's because," replied another, "horses are stolen and oxen are not."

"Then why is it," rejoined the first, "that in those places to which the stolen horses are taken, there are also more oxen than horses?"

"That's because," replied the other, "horses are stolen from those places also."

And thus a difficult question found a simple answer.

THE TELEGRAPH

Two large vehicles arrived in Chelem one day, laden with long spiked logs, rolls of wire, ladders and tools. There were men in the vehicles who set to work at once, planting the logs at regular intervals along the road, and stringing the wire from one log to another.

The people of Chelem were thrown into a furor, bordering on panic.

"What are they doing?" was the whispered question that ran from mouth to ear.

But no one knew, and all eyes turned to Lemach ben Lekish. Lemach answered without hesitation.

"They are putting up a telegraph system for Chelem," he told them.

"And what is that?" they demanded.

"Suppose," Lemach explained, "your wife has gone to visit her aunt in the big city a hundred miles away and you want her to come home at once. So you send her a telegram and in one hour she is on the way to Chelem."

"In one hour!" they marvelled.

"That is all it takes," Lemach assured them.

"But how? How is it done?" they insisted.

Lemach became lost in thought.

"It's very simple," said he. "You touch the wire in Chelem and something sounds in the big city, and that's how they know."

But one skeptic knitted his brow.

"My head," he declared, "doesn't take it in."

But just then a stray dog appeared, and seeing the crowd, he was about to make off, when Lemach whistled to him. The dog stopped in amazement: there was a kindly note in Lemach's call to which he was unaccustomed. He hesitated and then, in somewhat gingerly fashion, approached the philosopher.

"Look," said Lemach solemnly. "Here is the dog's rear: that's Chelem. Here is his head: that's the big city. And here is his tail: that's the telegraph. Now see what I do!"

And Lemach gave the dog's tail a violent pull. The dog uttered a shrill yelp and ran away.

"That's how the telegraph works," Lemach concluded. "You pull it in Chelem and you hear it in the big city a hundred miles away!"

And everybody understood and marvelled at the wisdom of Lemach ben Lekish.

GOOD TIDINGS FOR THE POOR

It was once observed that Lemach's face became as though illumined, and his brother philosophers realized that he had made a new discovery.

"What is it? What is it?" they asked.

"Thank Heaven!" he answered. "From now on every poor man will eat cream and every rich man will drink sour-milk. I've discovered how to do it.

"It's very simple," he continued solemnly as they crowded around him, "let a decree be issued in Chelem that from now on sour-milk shall be called cream and cream sour-milk!"

OPTICAL ILLUSION

The philosophers of Chelem could hold their own in any field of human knowledge, including the realm of political economy. Such complicated subjects as the monetary systems of nations held no terrors for them.

"It has been definitely established," said Lekish ben Lemach on one occasion, "that there is only one large gold piece in the country and it constantly changes hands. This process is called circulation."

"It's not so," objected one of his audience. "I once saw two gold pieces in the hands of two individuals at the same time."

Lekish wrinkled his brow.

"That," he declared finally, "was an optical illusion, produced by the speed of the circulation," a reply which convinced even the skeptic.

ALL IS VANITY

Among the philosophers of Chelem, the matter of illusions was a frequent subject of discourse. One Sabbath afternoon in winter they talked about the vanity of all things, and one of them even went so far as to maintain that all things were nothing but illusions—mirages of the senses, and that nothing exists in reality.

That night one of the cénacle was unable to sleep. He got up and paced his room in the dark.

"Yes, indeed," he said to himself. "All things are only an illusion—an empty dream. There is no heaven and no earth, no light and no darkness, no me and no you."

And as he walked he ran into the stove and barked his shins. The pain was formidable.

"It seems," said he to himself sadly, "that there is such a thing as a stove after all!"

HEREDITY

Nor was the science of genetics and heredity a *terra incognita* to the Chelem philosophers as the following conversation, fully authenticated, proves.

Said one to another:

"Strange that my beard is so thin. My grandfather, may he rest in peace, had a long thick beard like a forest."

"May it not be," replied the other, "that you take after your grandmother and not after your grandfather?"

The first pondered the question deeply.

"You are right," said he finally, "I distinctly remember that my grandmother had a very thin beard."

OFFSPRING AND OMELETTES

"I am thinking," a Chelem philosopher once said to another, "that I have found a flaw in the order of creation. In my opinion it would have been better if the way of the woman in bearing offspring were the same as the way of the hen."

"Indeed!" said the second philosopher.

"Yes," continued the first, "I would have ordered it that a woman should also lay eggs."

"But why?" asked the other.

"Why, you ask? Because that way would be much better for us—the men."

"Really?" the second philosopher wondered.

"Yes, indeed!" said the first. "Sometimes a man wants to beget sons and daughters. So he says to his wife: 'Take your eggs and hatch them!' Another time a man—well, a man is just hungry. So he says to his wife: 'Take your eggs and make me an omelette!' "

TWO WORDS UNSPOKEN

There was one among the philosophers of Chelem who was a fatalist, and he often drew on his own experience to prove his contention that a man's destiny was fixed and immutable.

"Listen to what happened to me to-day," he once reported to his fellow-thinkers. "For no reason that I can explain, I walked into the bank. Behind the windows sat individuals with piles of papers before them. They didn't even look at me. At one of the windows stood a man with a heap of money which he was counting, and this man did look at me. I began to feel very strange—hot and cold at the same time. 'Something wonderful is about to happen to you,' said I to myself, 'your destiny is upon you.' And I realized that everything depended on two words, two words which the man at the window might utter, two words which might raise me up and remove all burdens from me for the rest of my life. But did the man at the window say those two words? He did not! It was not ordained that he should. Alas, it was not to be!"

"And what could the man have said?" the philosopher was asked.

"What could he have said?" the fatalist replied. "Two words—no more! He could have said: 'Yankel, take!' "

ESTABLISHING IDENTITY

Who will deny that philosophy is a real friend to man? But everything real, no matter how good, is dogged by a shadow, and the shadow that dogs philosophy is skepticism.

A disturbing thought once assailed the mind of one of the thinkers of Chelem.

"How is a man known in the market-place?" he asked himself.

"By his clothes," he straightway answered.

"But in the bath-house," he continued. "In the bath-house everybody is naked. There is danger, therefore, that a man may lose his identity!"

On Friday, when every man of Chelem went to the bath-house in preparation for the Sabbath, the philosopher was afraid to go. But the holy Sabbath! How can a man fail in his ablutions for the Sabbath? So he took a red thread, tied it to his foot, and proceeded to the bath-house.

"Now I am safe!" he assured himself. "Now I cannot be mistaken for another."

He rubbed himself with more than usual energy and failed to note that during the process the thread slipped from his foot, and was picked up by his neighbor. The latter, recognizing the virtue of the red thread, tied it to his own foot.

The philosopher, having completed his ablutions, looked down, and behold! his thread was gone! And looking around he saw a red thread on the foot of his neighbor.

"Friend," said the unhappy philosopher, "I have never seen you before, but I know who you are. You are I. And now that I have told you who you are, would you not be good enough to tell me who I am?"

IRREPARABLE LOSS

The same philosopher once stepped into a shop to buy himself a new hat for Passover. He stood before the merchant rummaging into one pocket after another.

"What is it?" the merchant asked. "You've lost something?"

"I took the measurements of my head before I left home and wrote them down on paper," said the thinker, "and now, alas! the paper is lost!"

HE WAS ONCE BEAUTIFUL

It is reported of the same philosopher that his features were singularly ungainly, and when the *Shadchen* brought him before the maiden whom he was to wed, she looked at his features with an expression of incredulity.

"You look at me thus," said he, "because I am so ugly. But let it be known to you that I was not born ugly. In fact, I was born very beautiful. But I was put into the hands of a mean and envious nurse who exchanged me for another."

The maiden's sympathies, it should be noted, were deeply touched and she agreed to marry him.

A PHILOSOPHER ABROAD

It happened once that Lemach ben Lekish, the dean of the Chelem philosophers, fell into a mood of melancholy. For days and nights he had pondered on the higher mysteries, on life and death, on things that "eye hath not seen nor ear ever heard," and many were the questions that even he was unable to answer. And early one morning he said to his wife:

"Gittele, I have come to the limit of my wisdom. I will now go to foreign lands. I will seek out the wisest of the wise and lay my questions before them."

"How will you travel to foreign lands?" asked Gittele. "You have no passport."

Lemach wrinkled his brow and found the answer.

"My good friend Lekish ben Lemach," said he, "has a passport. Our names are very much alike and I will use his."

Gittele wept profusely, but in the end she accepted her husband's resolve as an edict from on high. Lemach obtained his friend's passport and set out for the frontier.

"Remember," was Gittele's last admonition. "Your name is not Lemach ben Lekish, but Lekish ben Lemach."

"The name, yes, of course," said Lemach with the absent air that marks every genuine thinker, "Lemach ben Lekish—no, not Lemach ben Lekish, of course not!"

And realizing the gravity of the matter, he kept reiterating in his mind as he travelled towards the border:

"Lemach ben Lekish—no! Not Lemach ben Lekish, of course not!"

And finally he reached the frontier, and a guard stood there and ordered him to stop. The man had a fierce up-curling moustache, and in his hand he held an instrument which Lemach knew was capable of dealing death.

"Passport!" the guard snapped.

Lemach produced the document.

"Your name!" the man demanded.

"My name—yes—my name. Lemach ben Lekish—certainly not!" Lemach replied.

THE WATCHMAN

Lemach ben Lekish came to the capital of the foreign land and in one of the squares he saw a great building. Never in his life had he seen such an immense structure!

"Good friend," said he to a passer-by, "what building is that?"

"It's the government bank," said the man.

"And it's full of money?" asked Lemach.

"Every nook and corner of it—millions and millions!"

"And who is the soldier with the gun near the door?"

"He keeps watch over the money."

"Isn't there danger that the soldier himself will steal the money?" asked Lemach.

"It's all put away in big iron boxes and double-locked and bolted with iron bars. No thief could open them."

"In that case," said Lemach, "what need is there for the soldier?"

But the man had become impatient.

"I don't know," he declared, "perhaps you can answer the questions yourself."

Lemach ben Lekish looked hard at the soldier and thought very deeply.

"It's clear," said he finally, "that this soldier is really a thief, and he is stationed here to keep him from robbing other places."

HAT AND GLOVES

Nor did Lemach return to Chelem empty-handed. He brought a variety of things that bespoke the greatness of the capital, and among them a newspaper. The thing in the newspaper that aroused most curiosity was a big advertisement of a clothing store showing the picture of a man wearing a straw hat and gloves.

"This is strange," said the philosophers of Chelem. "If the season of the year is winter, why is he wearing a straw hat? If it's summer, why is he wearing gloves?"

At last Lemach himself found the answer!

"It's summer!" he declared. "And why is he wearing gloves? Because he is going out to pluck nettles!"

THE *MELAMED* AND THE CZAR

In the chronicles of Chelem there is proof that the town was once visited by the Czar himself! And to silence all skeptics let the following be cited from the record concerning the *melamed* of Chelem, and his friend the philosopher, Lemach ben Lekish.

The *melamed*, it appears, made it a practice to put away a small part of his earnings and in time he was able to build himself a little house. But soon enough he learned how true are the words of the sage who said: "The more property, the more anxiety."

Into the humble abode of the *melamed* once strode a huge official in uniform who took a stamped paper out of a portfolio and in a loud voice proclaimed:

"His Majesty, the Czar, commands you to pay one ruble!"

The terrified *melamed* searched in a hidden nook, found the sum demanded and gave it to the man who pocketed it and departed. A little later the *melamed* recovered from his daze, and wondered greatly over what had befallen him. Unable to answer the questions that pounded on his brain, he went to his friend, the deep thinker, Lemach ben Lekish.

He found Lemach sunk in meditation and, after rousing him, related the strange visit of the official.

"I understand everything," said the *melamed*, "but there are three questions that I am unable to answer. First: How does the Czar know my name? Second: What need has the Czar of my ruble? Isn't he rich enough without it? Third: In order to collect my ruble the Czar sends a man from the capital to Chelem. Doesn't it cost more than a ruble to ride from the capital to Chelem and from Chelem back to the capital?"

Lemach ben Lekish didn't answer at once. It was not his way. He meditated a long time in silence, then turned to his friend with the assurance of a man who knows he is standing on firm ground.

"Three questions, three answers," he began in the terse style of the true thinker. "First: How does the Czar know your name? The answer is simple enough. Do you remember the Czar's visit to Chelem last year? You and I stood together by the side of the road, waiting for the Czar's carriage to pass. 'Motel Melamed,' I said to you, 'here comes the carriage of the Czar!' No doubt, the Czar heard me say it and wrote your name down in his notebook. Now for the second question: Why does the Czar need your ruble? The answer to that is also simple. There is a correspondence between the Kingdom of earth and the Kingdom of Heaven. The Talmud says: 'The governance of the earth is like the governance of Heaven.' The King of Heaven, blessed be He, is holiness itself; nevertheless He is glad to hear you say 'Holy, holy, holy!' In the same way the Czar is glad to have your ruble. And now we come to your third question. You are mistaken if you think the man came to Chelem just for your ruble. You have no understanding of state matters. Listen and learn. That man, you should know, was a soldier in the capital; and when his period of service was over he went to say goodbye to the Czar. In the course of conversation the man mentioned the fact that he was going to Chelem. 'To Chelem?' said the Czar. 'In that case, do me a favor. There is a *melamed* in Chelem who owes me a ruble. Collect the ruble from him and send it to me.'"

"Lemach," said the *melamed*, "all that men say about you is only half the truth. You are the ornament of Chelem. You are wisdom itself."

Strange Journey of Lekish ben Lemach

It was well-known in Chelem that there was something peculiar about the philosopher, Lekish ben Lemach. He lived with his wife and children, to all appearances like any other Chelemite, but in reality Lekish waited. He waited for the real head of his household to arrive. Yes, the real head, as though he himself were not the head of his household. Every day Lekish expected his arrival.

Lekish, it should be said at the outset, was inordinately proud of his native city, Chelem. He was convinced that no other city, not even the capital, was superior to it. He had no patience with those who sang the praises of other cities, belittling Chelem expressly or by implication. Whenever such frivolous talk was heard in the circle of deep thinkers around the synagogue stove, a little smile would curl up from the beard of Lekish ben Lemach which everybody understood. And it happened one fateful day that Getzel the *shadchen*, who had visited the capital and was brimming over with what he had seen there, was annoyed by that smile, and turning on Lekish, he said:

"Why don't you go there and see for yourself?"

"I will," said Lekish, nor did he realize how those two words were going to affect the course of his life.

The following day Lekish set out for the big city. He tightened the belt of his breeches, tied his girdle around his waist and slung over his shoulder a little bundle containing his *talis* and *tefilin* as well as a scant supply of bread and cheese, for it is well known that the material needs of the genuine philosopher are modest. It was a pilgrimage in reverse that Lekish embarked upon, for its purpose was to vindicate the shrine from which he departed rather than to worship at the goal for which he was bound.

The day was hot and heavy, but the heart of Lekish ben Lemach was light and his step springy. For a good distance the road was level, then as it turned and sloped gently downward, the city of Chelem became lost to view. Lekish trudged on. The sun mounted higher and it became still hotter. Peasant carts rumbled by and raised clouds of dust on the road.

Now the sun stood overhead and Lekish came to a crossroad. Near it rose a broad sycamore and a little brook gurgled over gray and golden pebbles. It was an alluring spot, and the same moment Lekish became aware that he was hungry. He washed his hands in the brook, pronounced the blessing, and ate of his bread and cheese. Then he drank from the brook and chanted grace.

"It's only right that I should rest here a little," said Lekish. He sat down in the shade of the tree, his back against the trunk, pervaded by a drowsy sense of well-being. His eye-lids drooped and his thoughts wandered off into the haze of sleep.

Suddenly Lekish ben Lemach roused himself. A disquieting thought smote upon his mind.

"If I fall asleep, how will I know what direction to follow when I wake up?" he asked himself.

Now Lekish was wide awake, and sat beneath the tree and pondered. The wise men of Chelem whom he might have consulted in his dilemma were far away, and Lekish had to rely on his own resources. But they rose to the occasion and he found the solution he sought. The solution was exceedingly simple, as indeed all great inventions are. Lekish ben Lemach took off his shoes, and put them down on the road with the toes pointing toward the big city for which he was bound.

"Now, I'm safe," said he with that vast complacency which sometimes comes over a philosopher. "When I wake up I'll know what direction to take!" And Lekish sat down again beneath the tree, and almost immediately fell asleep.

Lemach slept, but all around him the world was teeming with wakeful life. The ants at his feet were heaving and struggling with the burdens they carried to their lairs; the birds darted about seeking subsistence in the air, in the trees and on the ground, and wagons and carts rolled by in both directions, bearing the good fruits of the farms to the cities and the ingenious devices of the cities to the farms. And it happened that a wagon going to Chelem, heaped

high with stalks of green peas, rolled past near the
philosopher's shoes. And some of the stalks that hung
down low swept the road and, as the wagon moved
slowly by, they caught the philosopher's shoes and
turned them completely around. Such was the strange
thing that leaped from the lap of destiny while
Lekish ben Lemach slept.

Lekish woke up refreshed and a happy smile lay
hidden deep in his beard. He saw his shoes standing
where he left them, took careful note of the direction
in which they pointed, and put them again on his
feet.

"Many uses," he mused, "are hidden in things, of
which the simple are not aware. But the man to whom
God has granted wisdom, discovers them."

Lekish ben Lemach tightened his belt, looked to
the knot in his girdle, took up his bundle, and resumed his journey. He hoped to reach the capital by
nightfall, but great was his surprise when, as the
road took a turn, he saw it plainly in the distance
and not far off.

"So that's the capital!" said Lekish to himself view-
ing it from the road. "It's not so big. In fact, it's not
any bigger than Chelem. But that's how men are.
The thing that is not theirs always appears to them
to be bigger and better and finer."

Lekish walked on and came to the first straggling
houses of the outskirts.

"What is there about these houses," said he, "that
makes them better than the houses on the outskirts of
Chelem? It seems to me they are no better!"

Now he entered the city itself and looked around at the streets and houses.

"I swear," said he, "I have seen streets and houses like these in Chelem also! The streets are narrow and crooked and the houses need new roofs. And even the goats nibbling at the fences are like the goats in Chelem!"

He reached the market-place and what he saw there filled him with a sense of wonder and triumph.

"Blessed art thou, O Chelem!" he cried. "Not even the capital can boast a better market-place than yours. Everything here may also be found in yours! The same stalls, the same stands, the same well in the center, the same hollow log where the goats and chickens quench their thirst. Chelem, my Chelem, you are vindicated."

But Lekish ben Lemach was still unsatisfied. He was thirsty for some more draughts of triumph.

"Friend!" he cried to one who ran towards him, his coat-tails flying and perspiration dripping from his forehead, "tell me, are there any synagogues in this city?"

The man stopped in amazement and Lekish had to repeat the question.

"How then?" the man answered. "Everywhere! Everywhere!"

"Take me to the biggest!" said Lekish.

The man who had been rushing and sweating but really had nothing to do, took Lekish ben Lemach to the place he desired to see.

"Now blessed be the name of the Lord of Hosts for ever and ever!" Lekish exclaimed. "The biggest synagogue of the capital is no bigger and finer than the Great Synagogue of Chelem!"

Lekish went out and continued his journey through the streets of the city. Towards nightfall he came upon a street that was strangely like his own. He went on and came to a house that was also like his own. He entered the house and sat down to rest, feeling tired and bewildered.

"Where is the master of this house?" said he to a woman who came in carrying a market bag.

"Is this the best joke you can think up, philosopher mine?" the woman asked.

She set food before him, children came into the house, and they all ate.

"Everything in this city is exactly as in Chelem," he mused. "It's not true that there is a finer city in the world than Chelem. But where is the master of this house?

"He is sure to come soon," said Lekish to himself after eating and chanting grace. "I want very much to see him. I'll stay here and wait for him."

But that night the master of the house failed to come. Nor did he come on the morrow, nor on the days that followed.

And Lekish ben Lemach, the philosopher of Chelem, continues to live in that house with the woman and the children. Lekish is happy and contented, for Chelem, the city of his pride and love, triumphed against her traducers. But every now and then he turns to the woman who brings him his food and says:

"When will the master of the house come home? Isn't he ever going to come?"

Napoleon and the Tailor of Chelem

In Russia, as everybody knows, the great Napoleon had a bad time of it. The fact is he had to flee for his life! And one day, as he was running through Russia he came to Chelem and a troop of Russians were hard on his heels. Seeing that things had come to a desperate pass, Napoleon ran into the nearest house and cried aloud:

"Save me! There are people who want to murder me!"

Now in that house in Chelem there lived a tailor, and the tailor was seated on his table stabbing away with his needle. The tailor had never seen Napoleon before, but he asked no questions. A man in mortal danger must be helped! So he said quickly to Napoleon:

"Here, get into this bed, and I'll cover you up and no one will find you!"

Napoleon did as he was told, for there are times when an emperor must lie down in the bed of a tailor! And the tailor spread a heavy feather-bed over him, then threw another feather-bed over the first, and a third over the second, and a fourth over the third.

Did Napoleon sweat? He did, but there are times when even an emperor must sweat!

In no time, however, three Russians armed with spears burst into the tailor's house.

"Has any one come into your house?" they demanded. "Tell us quick!"

"In my house?" said the tailor who, being a Chelemite, was no fool, "who should come into my house?"

The Russians looked here, there, and everywhere, and before leaving, just to make sure, they plunged their spears a number of times through the feather-beds. Then, not to lose time in vain search, they went away.

In a little while, Napoleon stuck his head out from under the feather-beds and his face was as white as a sheet.

"Are they gone?" he asked.

"Yes," said the tailor. "You can come out."

Napoleon jumped off the bed and stood up straight before the tailor.

"I want to inform you," said he, "that I am the Emperor Napoleon! You have saved me from certain death. In return I give you leave to ask me for three things and they will be granted. Now ask—and remember, any three things!"

Was there ever a tailor in such a situation? Napoleon himself! What should he ask him for? He thought and thought and finally said:

"Your majesty, my roof has been leaking for two years. Please order it to be mended."

Napoleon looked at the tailor with hard contempt.

"Is that all you can think of asking of me, Napoleon?" he demanded. "Very well! Your roof shall be mended. Now ask again! And remember, only two more things."

The tailor twisted his beard and thought and thought. He found the second request even harder than the first. But suddenly he saw a great light!

"Your majesty," he said, "my wife and I have been married for thirty years and she is still wearing the same wig that she got on her wedding day. And she nags me to death about it: she wants a new wig. Please order a new wig for my wife, your majesty."

"Very well," said Napoleon with a tone of withering sarcasm. "Your roof shall be mended and your wife shall have a new wig. But remember, tailor, I am the Emperor Napoleon and you can ask me one thing more! Now let it be something—something worthwhile!"

But now the tailor was at the end of his wits. He could think of nothing more to ask. He needed nothing! He twisted his beard and chewed it, but he could think of nothing! The tailor began to feel afraid.

"Must I—must I ask for something?" he stammered.

"You must!" said Napoleon.

"Well, if I must," said the tailor, "I will ask you to tell me how you felt when the Russians drove their spears through the feather-beds!"

Napoleon looked at the tailor with amazement and wrath.

"How dare you ask me such a question?" he cried.

"It's unheard of! For such *chutzpah* I will order you to be shot!"

He called in three of his soldiers, and the poor tailor was cast into irons and taken away. What a situation for a tailor to be in!

"Where are you taking me?" he begged.

"Never mind where," they told him, "early tomorrow morning you will be shot."

All night long the tailor wept and prayed and confessed his sins. A little before dawn he was taken out and tied to a tree. Three soldiers took their stand in front of him with loaded guns. An officer stood near them with a watch in his hand.

The tailor was already more dead than alive. He shook in every limb and the perspiration flowed down his body in streams. One second he was hot, the next he was cold. Is it necessary to describe in detail how a tailor would feel in such a situation?

"Now then," said the officer to the soldiers. "The moment has arrived. When I say three, you will fire!"

The soldiers lifted their guns and aimed.

"One!" said the officer.

"Two!" said the officer.

But before he could say "three," the sound of galloping hoofs was heard and a mighty general on horseback with medals on his chest burst upon the scene.

"Don't shoot!" he cried to the soldiers. And to the tailor he said:

"The emperor pardons you, and he asked me to give you this letter."

And in Napoleon's letter the tailor read the following words:

"You want to know how I felt under the feather-beds? I felt exactly as you felt just now."

And this too can be found in the Chronicles of Chelem.

RICH MAN, POOR MAN

RICH MAN, POOR MAN

In the waiting room of a famous Chassidic rabbi sat a rich man and a poor man. The rich man was ushered in first and it was almost an hour before he came out. The poor man followed and was given only a few minutes.

"Rabbi," said the poor man before going out, "are you not discriminating between the rich and the poor?"

"Foolish man!" said the rabbi. "When you came in I knew you were a poor man as soon as I looked at you, but the other—I had to talk to him an hour before I knew he was as poor as you."

RECIPE FOR ETERNAL LIFE

"If you want to live forever," said a wit to a rich man, "come and live in my town."

"Doesn't anybody die in your town?" said the other.

"Yes, indeed," replied the wit. "But it has never happened yet that a rich man should die there!"

HE STOOPS TO CONQUER

A famous rabbi, who was a master in the art of getting money from the rich for the benefit of the poor, was once asked:

"How does a man of your standing prevail on himself to stoop before the rich swine of this town? Does it accord with your dignity to demean yourself before them?"

"My son," replied the sage, "it is all in the order of nature. Look now, there is no creature on earth more excellent than man, and few creatures more lowly than the cow. Nevertheless, a man has to stoop before the cow when he wants to milk her!"

FOR THE POOR

There was once a rich miser who, it so happened, was an ardent follower of a famous Chassidic rabbi. The miser came to visit his mentor and the rabbi solemnly enjoined him to eat only of the best meat, fish, and fowl, and to drink the best wines.

The other followers of the rabbi thought it very strange.

"Rabbi," they said, "why are you so concerned about the good cheer of that miser?"

"I'm not concerned about him," the rabbi explained. "I'm concerned about the poor. If he himself eats nothing but bread and water, can you expect him to think of the poor? But if he drinks the best wines and eats the best meats he may give bread to the poor."

SECOND NATURE

There was once a *shlemiel* who wanted very much to be a rich man, and on more than one occasion seemed to be on the point of attaining his ambition. But whenever he had a little saved up, he gave it away to the poor. The *shlemiel* couldn't understand it, and he was still more embittered when he saw a certain fellow-townsman of his grow richer and richer continually.

He decided finally to overcome his dislike of the man and go to him for advice.

"My friend," said the rich man, "your method is all wrong. You waste your substance on charity. A man who wants to be rich must make up his mind to be a swine for the first ten years."

"And after that?" asked the *shlemiel*.

"After that," replied the rich man, "it becomes second nature."

HIGH FEVER

In a certain town there lived a miserly rich man who never gave to the poor or to any of the communal institutions. Once this man became dangerously ill, and the community officials felt that their opportunity had come. They called on the rich man, spoke to him feelingly, and were successful. He promised them fifty rubles for charity!

Not long afterwards, the town learned with surprise that the man was well again. The officials paid him another visit, congratulated him on his recovery, and expressed the hope that he would pay his pledge.

"Chaye Rochel!" the man called to his wife. "Do you hear, Chaye Rochel? It's only now that I find out how sick I was. What high fever I must have had! I promised them fifty rubles!"

CONSOLATION FOR THE RICH

"There is no limit to the impudence of the paupers in this town!" said the wife of a rich man to her husband. "When we celebrate a happy occasion, we have to pay out to them. When they have a wedding or something, we again have to pay out!"

"Don't let it upset you, my dear," her husband consoled her. "It's true that this world belongs to the poor, but remember the World-to-Come is reserved for us!"

HE WEEPS

A rich man was being taken to his eternal home and his relatives followed the bier and wept. A stranger joined them and wept with the rest.

"Are you too a relative of the deceased?" they asked him.

"No," he answered, still weeping.

"Then why do you weep?"

"That's why," he replied.

POOR BUT GENEROUS

A certain *melamed* used to say: "If the Holy One, blessed be He, gave me ten thousand rubles, I would at once deduct a thousand and give it away as my tithe for the poor. And I say further, if He doesn't trust me to do so, let Him deduct the tithe himself and give me the balance."

SUSPICIOUS

"And how are you getting on in the world?" some one was asked.

"I suspect," he replied, "that I am getting rich."

"What do you mean you suspect?"

"I can't quite make it out," was the reply. "I haven't any money yet, but I feel that I am already very much of a swine."

HE PERSPIRED

A rich old miser became critically ill and the doctor prescribed a medicine with the following warning:

"If after taking this medicine, you perspire, it's a sign that you will get well. If you don't perspire, we can only put our trust in God."

The miser took the medicine, but failed to perspire. From mouth to mouth ran the whisper that the rich man was about to die.

"Let us call on him," said the rabbi to the worthies of the town. "Perhaps he will now repent of his ways and leave something for the needs of the community."

So they came to him, and found him indeed in a repentant mood. They brought paper and ink and the rabbi got ready to write.

"The synagogue," he said, "is badly in need of repairs."

"A hundred rubles for the synagogue," said the miser and groaned pitifully.

"The bath-house is tumbling down," said the rabbi.

"Fifty rubles for the bath-house," the miser groaned again and writhed.

"The widows' and orphans' fund is depleted," said the rabbi.

"A hundred—wait a minute, wait a minute!" the miser cried suddenly. "Cross it all out! I'm perspiring! I'm perspiring!"

IMPARTIAL

There were great demands on the Passover Fund that year and the collectors decided to call on the rich man for a contribution.

"I can't give you anything," he told them, "I have a poor brother."

And shortly afterwards the poor brother himself applied for help from the Fund.

"You?" they said to him. "You don't have to come to us! You have a rich brother."

"Yes," the poor man replied. "But I don't get anything from him."

So the collectors called on the miser again.

"You are not only a miser," they told him, "but also a deceiver. Your brother has just applied for charity!"

"I am no deceiver," said the miser. "I only told you I had a poor brother. And if," he continued, "I don't give anything to my own brother, do you suppose I'll give to strangers?"

A *MELAMED*, HIS GOAT, AND HIS CHICKENS

Year after year the household of a certain *melamed* increased, the quarters remained the same, until at last the congestion was more than he could bear. So he went to the rabbi for advice.

"Have you a goat?" asked the old rabbi.

"How then?" said the *melamed*. "Every *melamed* has a goat!"

"Take the animal into your dwelling."

"But—but—" the *melamed* stammered.

"Will you do as I say!"

"Yes," said the *melamed*, and he brought the goat into his house.

After the first surprise, the silly animal got used to it, but the others didn't. Again the *melamed* came to the rabbi.

"I have obeyed your command," said he, "but things are worse than ever."

"Have you any chickens?" asked the old rabbi.

"A few," said the *melamed*, with a sinking of the heart.

"Bring them into your house," said the rabbi.

"Rabbi," the *melamed* began.

"Will you do as I say!" the rabbi commanded.

The *melamed* brought his chickens into his house. The birds perched on every point of vantage and felt quite at home.

The *melamed* returned to the rabbi and wept.

"Very bad, my son, isn't it?" said the old rabbi.

"It's—the end of the world!" said the *melamed*.

"Very well, then. Now go home and drive out the goat and chickens, and come to me again to-morrow."

The following day the *melamed* stood before the rabbi and his face was beaming.

"Rabbi!" said he, "my house, it's a paradise!"

"WHAT TIME IS IT?"

The night-watchman in the pawn-shop was startled by the sudden ringing of the bell. He ran to the door, and looked through the small opening.

"What do you want?" he demanded of someone who stood on the other side.

"I want to know what time it is," the man replied.

"So you had to come here?" the watchman cried.

"You see," the other replied. "I've got my watch here. It's hanging right over the counter."

ALSO A VICTIM

Most of the little town went up in flames and smoke, and in the neighboring towns money and clothing were distributed to the victims of the fire. Among those who applied for relief was one whose house was untouched.

"What are you doing here?" he was asked. "You haven't lost anything?"

"It's true," he answered. "But do you realize how frightened I was?"

HERSHEL KNOWS BETTER

Hershel Ostropoler, the famous wag and prankster, was devoted to the bottle and it kept him so poor that he had to use his floor for a bed and his fist for a pillow.

"Hershel," they said to him once, "why don't you stop wasting your substance on drink and buy yourself at least a pillow to lay your head on?"

"Not I," said Hershel. "I know all about your pillows. Once, just to assure myself, I placed a feather under my head before falling asleep. I got up the next morning with a stiff neck and a headache. So I reasoned: if a single feather can play so much havoc, what will a whole pillow do?"

HUMILIATED!

Strange as it may sound, Hershel's domicile was visited one night by thieves.

"Get up!" his wife whispered in his ear. "There are thieves in the house!"

"I know it," Hershel replied, "but I can't get up. I'm burning with shame. There isn't a thing in the house worth taking!"

A MATTER OF LUCK

The next time a thief visited him, Hershel jumped up and seized the intruder. The thief tried to escape.

"Don't try to run away!" said Hershel. "Let me join you in your search. Perhaps your luck is better than mine!"

A GOOD BEGINNING

"Hershel," a neighbor asked him one day before the Passover feast, "how far have you gone with your Passover preparations?"

"Half of them are done," said Hershel.

"How do you mean that?" asked the neighbor.

"The leaven," Hershel explained, "has been removed from the house. All I have to do is to bring in the matzo and the other Passover provisions."

NO LAUGHING MATTER

Motke Chabad was a famous *shlemiel* and a day came when all his ventures ended in failure. He went to call on the head of the community.

"If the community doesn't support me," he threatened, "I will become a hat maker!"

"And what if you will?" he was asked.

"Don't you realize what would happen?" asked Motke. "Don't you know that if I become a hat maker, every child in the city will be born without a head?"

RECIPE FOR HAPPINESS

"You ask me why I limp and groan, my friend? I'll tell you. It's because my shoes are tight. Yes, my feet are as in a vise. Why do I wear them, you ask? I'll tell you why. My business is going to the dogs, my creditors are hounding me, my rent is unpaid, my daughters are marriageable and without prospects, and my wife is an unbearable nag. I come home and my troubles sweep over me like a flood. I feel that life isn't worth living. What, then, do I do? My friend, I sit down and take off my shoes. Yes, I take these mean things off my burning feet, and what joy is mine, what happiness!"

IT WOULDN'T PAY

The rich man of the town chanced to meet the tailor and noticed that the poor man was wearing a torn and dilapidated *kaftan*. Said he to the tailor:

"I can't understand it. You are yourself a tailor. Why don't you mend your own clothes?"

"Where will I find the time?" replied the tailor. "Now I have to make a coat for the *poretz*, now a pair of trousers for the rabbi, and so on. For myself I never have the time."

The rich man was moved by the tailor's words. He handed him a ruble and said:

"Here is something for your time. Take it and patch up your *kaftan*."

Five days later he met the tailor again and in the same dilapidated *kaftan*.

"What does it mean?" said he. "Why didn't you mend your *kaftan*?"

"I'll tell you," said the tailor. "I figured out that at that price it wouldn't pay me to do it."

FROGS

The way was long, the sun hot, the road dusty. With heavy heart, a *melamed* urged on his goat: he was taking it to the nearest town in order to sell it. The *melamed* became suddenly aware that he was fond of the foolish creature, but what alternative had he? Was it right to keep the goat and starve for bread with his wife and children? Man and beast plodded wearily along, the man giving vent to his sorrows in frequent groans.

A beggar appeared from nowhere and began following the man and the goat. The beggar looked even more woebegone than the *melamed*, and his groans were louder.

"What *chutzpah!*" said the *melamed*. And turning to the beggar he demanded:

"What right have you to groan so loud? Are your troubles greater than mine?"

"You have a goat!" said the beggar, "and I have nothing!"

"I have a goat!" said the *melamed* bitterly. "I'm a happy man! Yes, I'm a happy man!"

And just then a frog appeared from the roadside and jumped on in front of the wayfarers.

"Look here!" the *melamed* turned suddenly on the beggar. "I'll give you the goat! Just catch that frog and swallow it, and I'll give you my goat!"

The beggar ran forward, caught the frog, and swallowed it.

"Give me the goat," said he.

"Take it!" said the *melamed*.

Now the beggar was urging the beast along the road, the *melamed* following a short distance behind.

"What have I done?" said the *melamed* to himself and his heart sank. "What will my wife say? What will I bring home for my children to eat?" And groan after groan broke from his bosom as he plodded on after the beggar and the goat.

In the meantime a series of peculiar sensations visited the beggar in his entrails. The sweat broke on his forehead and his knees sagged. He turned fiercely on the *melamed*.

"What right have you to groan like that?" he demanded. "Do you, perhaps, consider your lot worse than mine?"

"You have the goat," said the *melamed*, "and I have nothing!"

"Indeed!" cried the beggar. "So you think I am a happy man! Oh, my entrails, my entrails!"

And just then a frog appeared from the side of the road and jumped on in front of the wayfarers.

"Look!" the beggar cried. "Do you see that frog? Catch it and swallow it, and you can have the goat again!"

The *melamed* at once caught the frog and swallowed it.

"Now give me the goat!" he cried.

"Take it," said the beggar.

Now the *melamed* had his goat again and urged it on along the hot and dusty road. Behind him walked the beggar, still groaning: "My entrails, my entrails!"

But now came the turn of the *melamed's* entrails where the frog produced a fierce commotion. Beggar and *melamed* groaned in concert. Neither resented the other's groans: now they understood each other.

At last they came to the town and halted. The two looked at each other pained and bewildered.

"Friend!" said the *melamed* to the beggar. "Tell

me, I pray you! Why did we two have to swallow frogs?"

"Why indeed?" the beggar replied.

And the two walked on together and groaned.

MELAMED'S LUCK

Once upon a time there was a duke who was very vain of his beard. It was indeed a handsome beard: broad and silken in appearance, and brilliant black in color. This nobleman always stroked his beard and it was clear to all men that the beard was his pride and joy.

But one day the king, who was out hunting with the duke, said to him:

"You needn't be so proud of your beard. I once saw an old *melamed* in a town not far from here whose beard was handsomer than yours."

The count smiled a proud, disdainful smile.

"So you don't believe me!" the king continued. "I'll tell you what I'll do. I'll have the *melamed* brought here, but you must promise that if his beard is finer than yours, you will pay him a thousand gold pieces."

The count agreed and the same day the king sent messengers to bring the *melamed* post-haste to the capital. The king told them nothing of the reason why he wanted the *melamed*, but they had performed similar errands for the king in the past, and knew just what to do. They seized the *melamed*, put him in chains, brought him to the capital, and threw him into prison.

The chief messenger presented himself to the king.

"Have you brought the *melamed?*" the king demanded.

"Yes, Your Majesty," the man replied.

"Is he safe and secure?"

"Yes, Your Majesty."

"Bring him before me to-morrow morning," the king commanded.

Early the following morning the messenger went to the jail to execute the king's command. Accompanied by the jailer, he entered the *melamed's* cell and looked hard at his beard. It was an extraordinary growth: it spread out in every direction almost hiding its owner's features, and reached down to his girdle. The messenger and jailer looked at it in amazement. Never had they seen such a beard!

"Is it proper for anything like that to be presented to His Majesty?" said the messenger. "Jailer," he continued, "call the barber and let him remove the prisoner's beard!"

And the jailer did as he was ordered.

THE NERVOUS TWIST

Yankel the shoemaker jumped suddenly into a fortune, an inheritance or whatever it was, and became the rich man of the town. He began to receive high honors, was made a trustee of the congregation, and not only was he accorded the best portions of

the Reading on the Sabbath, but he had the power
to decide who was to get the other portions. Now
in the same city it came to pass that a certain learned
and rich man lost his wealth and, it goes without
saying, everything that happened to the former shoemaker happened to the *lamdan* in reverse. Yankel,
moreover, avenged himself on the fallen rich man
and never gave him a portion of the Sabbath Reading. The *lamdan* was indignant and before long
adopted a peculiar method of retaliation. During
the Sabbath services, when Yankel, in all his gran-
deur, stood on the Bimah allotting the portions, the
lamdan stood up in his place and jerked his thumb
back and forth just as a shoemaker does when he
pulls his thread. Yankel felt greatly humiliated, and
when the *lamdan* persisted with his thumb-exercise
in the sight of all the congregation, Yankel couldn't
stand it and haled him before the judge. A trial took
place with lawyers and all the other accessories.
Now, the *lamdan's* lawyer hit upon a shrewd device.
He explained to the judge that his client suffered
from a nervous condition which made him jerk his
thumb in the manner that the former shoemaker
found so obnoxious. The *lamdan* was acquitted. On
the way home from the trial he approached the former shoemaker.

"Yankel," said he, "it's true, of course, as my lawyer
explained, that I am afflicted with a nervous disease.
But you, Yankel, you understand that little twist,
don't you?"

A *MELAMED* INTERFERES

It happened long ago when the French under Napoleon were invading Russia. They came to a town near the border and the *melamed* was walking home with two pails of water which he had drawn at the river. He lifted up his eyes, and behold, the French were coming! Now, it is well known that if you meet someone on the road who is carrying full pails you are going to have good luck.

"These soldiers," said the *melamed* to himself, "are coming against my king, and am I going to help them?"

So he poured the water out of his pails on the road before the enemy. When he came home, his wife saw the pails and asked why they were empty. The *melamed* told her but instead of approving she scolded him.

"If two powers fall out," said she, "do you have to interfere?"

THE WAY OF A HORSE

There was a wagoner who had a good horse, but the man was poor and oats came dear, so he decided to wean his animal away from the habit of eating. He began by cutting down his allowance of oats. Then he omitted his meals altogether one day a week, then two days a week, then three. The wagoner saw his experiment succeeding and rejoiced. In the midst of it all, the silly horse spoiled everything by dying. The poor man refused to be consoled. He stood over the beast, wept and cried:

"Another week or two, and all my worries would have been over, so you go and die!"

DELAY FULLY EXPLAINED

There was a merchant who had business in a neighboring town and he sent word to the wagoner on a Sunday to call for him on Monday. The wagoner came exactly a week later. The merchant was indignant and ordered him out of his house.

"Please," said the wagoner, "it's not my fault, and I did the best I could. Sunday you told me to come on Monday. Tuesday I forgot about it, and when I saw on Wednesday that I won't be able to come on Thursday, and Friday night I couldn't come on account of the Sabbath, and Sunday I mustn't come because you told me to come on Monday, I came to-day! So how am I to blame?"

THE HEROIC TAILOR

Ever hear the story of the heroic little tailor? It's very short. He was out walking one day and saw a fight. He didn't hesitate a moment. He whipped off his coat, rolled up his sleeves, jumped right in, got a fiery slap in the face, and ran away. That's the whole story.

OF COURSE!

"Name?"
"Isaac Levy."
"Place of birth?"
"Poland."
"Business?"
"Second-hand clothing."
"Religion?"
"Episcopalian, of course!"

WEALTH AND WISDOM

There was a certain wise man who was asked:
"What is more important, wealth or wisdom?"
"Wisdom," he replied.
"If so, why do the wise wait on the rich? Why
don't the rich wait on the wise?"
"Because," was the reply, "the wise, being wise,
understand the value of riches, but the rich, being
only rich, don't understand the value of wisdom."

BEGGAR MAN, THIEF

CAVIAR

The beggar looked so pitiful that the man slipped a whole ruble into his hand. Entering a restaurant a little while later, the generous man found the beggar seated at a table eating caviar. The man was indignant.

"Aren't you ashamed of yourself?" he said. "Begging on the streets and spending the alms you get for caviar!"

The beggar became indignant in his turn.

"Look here!" he cried. "Before I got the ruble, I *couldn't* eat caviar. Now that I have the ruble, I *mustn't* eat caviar. At that rate, when on earth *will* I eat caviar?"

WORTH ALL IT COSTS

Two kinds of bread, black and white, were served during the meal. The poor guest ate the white bread only. The master of the house noticed it and thought it a breach of etiquette which deserved a mild rebuke.

"Why," he turned to his guest, "don't you eat black bread also?"

"The white is better," the guest replied.

"But it costs more money," said the master of the house.

"It's worth it," the poor guest replied.

HE SUPPORTS HIM

It is an ancient and honorable custom for house-holders to bring home from the synagogue on Friday night some poor wayfarer and entertain him over the Sabbath.

In observance of this custom a man was walking home one Friday night with his Sabbath guest, when, not far from his door-step, he became aware that someone was trailing them.

"Who is that?" he asked his guest.

"It's my son-in-law," the beggar explained. "I am supporting him."

TEAM-WORK

There were two who worked together as follows:

They presented themselves before the wealthy man of the town and one of them, pointing to the other, said with great solemnity:

"This man is descended from saints and scholars and he is destitute."

Whereupon the rich man handed the illustrious scion a handsome gift.

"A little something for my trouble," said the first.

"Your trouble?"

"Of course," the beggar explained. "Haven't I brought him to your house?"

ROBBING THE POOR

There was a certain *shnorrer* who used to receive a handsome stipend every year from the banker of the town—not less than 500 crowns. One year he received only half the amount. The beggar hastened to his patron.

"What's the meaning of this?" he asked.

"I am having unusual expenses this year," the banker explained. "My son has become engaged to an actress and it's costing me a lot of money."

"This is unheard of!" the beggar cried. "If he wants to support an actress, that's his business. But let him do it with his own money, not mine!"

NO CREDIT

The beggar told a pathetic tale and it made an impression on his hearer.

"I want to help you," said he, "but you meet me at an unfortunate moment. I am absolutely without cash. Could you come to-morrow?"

"Impossible," said the beggar.

"Why not?"

"I have lost too much already by extending credit."

LEAVE IT TO HIM

Seven o'clock in the morning the banker of the town was awakened by a loud knocking on the street door of his house. Quickly he opened the door and before him stood a beggar, asking for alms.

"How dare you disturb me so early in the morning?" the banker demanded.

"My dear sir," the beggar replied, "I don't question your competence in the matter of banking, but when it comes to begging, please leave it to me."

A SLIGHT OBSTACLE

"I could have earned a hundred rubles yesterday," said a beggar to his cronies.

"How?" they asked him.

"A rich lady offered to pay me that sum if she could look at me."

"Just look at you?"

"That's all."

"And you refused?"

"I didn't, but she was blind in both eyes."

AN OMELET

Said a beggar to his wife:

"I want you to make me an omelet. I am curious to know what there is about it that rich people like so much."

Said his wife:

"We have no eggs."

"What of that?" said the man. "Can't you make an omelet without eggs?"

"We have no butter," said the woman.

"Listen to her!" the beggar mocked. "Butter she needs!"

"I haven't even a pan," said the woman.

"We have red coals, haven't we?" said the beggar.

The woman took some flour, poured water over it, mixed it and laid the paste on the coals. It burned to soot at the bottom and remained raw at the top. The beggar took some into his mouth and spat out.

"Those rich!" he jeered. "The things they like! Does anyone understand them?"

THE LAST POCKET

A group of people stood around a weeping beggar in the market-place.

"What's wrong?" someone asked.

"I had one coin," said the beggar, "and I've lost it."

"Have you searched in all your pockets?"

"Yes."

"Look again," the beggar was told.

He obeyed. Methodically he went through his pockets and searched.

"It's gone!" he declared.

"Wait a minute," said one of the group who observed him closely. "You've skipped one of your pockets. Why don't you search that one also?"

"Oh, that one!" the beggar cried. "Oh, no! Not that one!"

"Why not?"

"Suppose," the beggar answered, "I search this last pocket and the coin isn't there!"

PLACE AND FORTUNE

Sender and Bender were two jolly beggars, friends of the dusty road, and they stopped one day at an inn and asked the owner for a night's lodging.

"You can both sleep on top of the oven," he told them. "But I'm having a wedding here to-night and I want you to have nothing to do with my guests."

Sender and Bender agreed, and before any of the guests arrived, the two had stretched out on the huge oven, and were fast asleep.

The guests arrived and began to make merry. The fiddles squeaked, the guests danced, and the bottle passed from hand to hand. The night wore on and their merriment increased. At last they took note of the two on the oven. The beggars lay facing the wall, their rears exposed to the wedding guests not without a suggestion of mockery and disdain. Some of the young swains held counsel together and agreed on what to do. They lifted one of their number who administered some lusty blows on the outside rear, which happened to be that of Sender. Everybody except Sender was highly pleased. The fiddles squeaked again and the wedding guests danced.

Sender had a premonition and awakened his partner.

"Bender," said he, "let's change places. Mine is a little too warm."

And the unsuspecting Bender complied.

As soon as the dance was over, the young swains got into another huddle.

"Let's do it again!" said one.

"Yes, let's do it again!" they agreed.

They lifted the same youth and he was about to begin when someone said:

"Wait a minute! Why the same one? Let the other one have it this time!"

The youth obeyed and his blows fell accurately and profusely on the rear of the inside sleeper. Again, with the exception of Sender, everybody, including Bender, was pleased.

"Sender," said Bender, "what are you thinking of?"

"I'm thinking," said Sender, "of a famous passage in the Talmud."

"And what is the passage?"

" 'A change of place brings a change of fortune,' " Sender quoted.

"And what is your opinion of that passage?" Bender inquired.

"Bender," said Sender, "my opinion is—shut your mouth and go to sleep."

THE IRON BRIDGE, REB TODROS!

There was a jolly beggar who came on Saturday night to Reb Todros, the rich man of the town, and began by telling him that his errand involved the life or death of a human being.

"Yours?" the rich man asked.

"No, yours," the beggar replied.

Reb Todros ordered his servant to bring drinks and cookies, and the beggar, after fortifying himself generously, explained as follows:

"I listened to the *maggid* this afternoon. He told us that in the end of days, two bridges will be built across the Great Sea, one of iron, the other of paper. The sinful nations will take the iron bridge, but will fall into the sea. Israel will take the paper bridge and go across it in safety. I pondered a long time over this prophecy, and I concluded finally that, as between iron and paper, in spite of what the *maggid* told us, iron is to be preferred. And I thought of you, Reb Todros, and I have come to warn you: Don't rely on miracles! Take the iron bridge, do you hear, Reb Todros? The iron bridge!"

SAME ADDRESS

In the market-place one day, two beggars became such a nuisance that the policeman arrested them. He took out his notebook and pencil.

"Name?" he asked one.

"Yankel ben Shmerel."

"Where do you live?"

"Nowhere. I have no home."

The policeman turned to the other.

"Name?"

"Shmerel ben Yankel."

"Address?"

"We are partners," the beggar replied, pointing to the other, "and we live together."

HARD TIMES!

"I managed to be admitted into Rothschild's home," one *shnorrer* boasted to another.

"Indeed!" said the second. "And how much did he give you?"

"Ten marks."

"That's all? I would have gotten fifty!"

"You are mistaken. I was glad enough to get the ten. Things are not so well with our friend Mr. Rothschild."

"Really? How do you know?"

"Would you believe it?" replied the first *shnorrer*. "I saw two of his daughters playing on one piano."

A BET

Said a beggar to Rothschild:

"Don't mistake me. I am not a beggar. I have come here on business."

"Business?"

"Yes, business. I want to make a bet with you. I want to bet you a hundred francs that I can obtain something that you can not."

The banker put a hundred francs on the table. The beggar picked them up and slipped them into his pocket.

"Your Excellency," he said, "I can get a pauper's certificate from the community. Can you get one?"

STYLE

The two beggars decided to call on Rothschild. Said the older to the younger:

"You wait for me on the sidewalk. I'll deal with Rothschild alone. I know how to handle these people."

He was actually admitted into the presence of the great banker, and after listening to him, Rothschild sent him to his secretary. The secretary sent him to the almoner. The almoner sent him to the bookkeeper. The bookkeeper sent him to the porter. The porter took the beggar by the collar and threw him out.

The beggar landed on the sidewalk near his partner.

"Nu," said the latter, "what did you get?"

"I can't say that I got anything," the beggar replied. "But shall I tell you something? The order in that establishment is simply magnificent!"

THE ROOSTER

It is a well-known fact that a *Yeshuvnik* will welcome a wayfarer of his own faith who may chance to visit him. One day, Yossel the *Yeshuvnik* saw on his threshold a long thin beggar with beard and earlocks. He opened his door wide and invited him to enter.

"Will you have the goodness to give me a bed for the night?" said the beggar.

"Gladly, gladly," said Yossel. "Come right in. And if you are hungry—"

"Hungry?" said the beggar with a wan smile. "There is a hole in my stomach as big as the void before creation."

"Zlate!" said Yossel calling to his wife, "there is a hungry Jew in the house! Don't lose a minute, and remember—the best of everything!"

Never had the beggar feasted so well and Yossel stood over him, waiting on him, and deriving *nachas* from the way the man ate. The beggar devoured everything with extraordinary speed, omitting to all appearances the process of mastication. And the quantity of food that he caused to vanish was astounding.

"You have, thank God, a good appetite," Yossel remarked, beaming on his guest.

"In the partition of the good things of life between the rich and the poor," the beggar managed to articulate, "the Holy One, blessed be He, observed even-handed justice. He gave the food to the rich and the appetite to the poor."

"He is wise, this beggar," said Yossel to himself. "A wise guest is an ornament to a household."

That night the beggar slept soundly and snored grandly, and when he was up in the morning he couldn't bear the thought of going away so soon.

"Will you permit me," said he to Yossel, "to sleep another night in your house?"

That's the way he put it, the shrewd beggar: "sleep another night!" As though it wasn't the food that was uppermost in his mind!

"Yes, of course, why not?" Yossel replied.

So the beggar stayed and he ate all day as if he was under sentence not to eat again for the rest of his life afterwards. And the following morning he was reluctant to ask his host for another day. It seemed to him that the *Yeshuvnik's* answer the previous morning had not been cordial enough. So he stayed without asking.

He stayed another day, and another, and another. On the fourth day he observed that the food was not so plentiful. On the fifth it was still less plentiful; on the sixth it was hardly sufficient. For the beggar's appetite, it should be made clear, suffered not the slightest diminution. This can only be stated; it cannot be explained.

"What is this?" said the beggar to his host on the seventh day. "Am I to starve here?"

"Believe me," said Yossel penitently. "It is not my fault. It's simply that the food is giving out. If you stay another day, I'll have nothing to give you. As for me and my Zlate, we are facing starvation."

"*Oy veh!*" cried the beggar. "You have nothing for tomorrow? Why didn't you tell me? Do you think I am the kind of a man who would rob people of their last morsel? Tomorrow morning I'll go!"

"Will you, really?" said Yossel and there were tears in his voice.

"Of course, I will!" declared the beggar. "Wake

me up very early, before dawn. I'm a weak man and I can't walk in the heat of the sun."

"I'll be sure to wake you," Yossel promised, and so the matter was settled.

The beggar went to bed and slept like a top. Why shouldn't he? His mind and his conscience were clear. The *Yeshuvnik* on the other hand was unable to sleep. To begin with, his conscience was not altogether clear: was it right to send the beggar away? In the second place, the *Yeshuvnik* was afraid he might fail to wake the beggar early enough, in which case the beggar might stay on. Wasn't he a weak man, unable to walk in the heat of the sun? So Yossel lay on his bed, awake and alert all night. And as soon as the first gray glimmer of dawn appeared he got up and proceeded to wake up his guest.

The beggar was still sound asleep and his snoring was impressive. Yossel took him by the shoulder and shook him.

"What? What is it?" asked the beggar out of his sleep.

"Get up!" cried Yossel in his ear. "The rooster has crowed already!"

The beggar sat bolt upright in bed.

"What? What's that you say?" he cried. "You still have a rooster? Then I stay!"

And the beggar stayed.

THE ACROBAT

There came to a certain town a poor Jew who looked for something to do for a living. But he found nothing, so he hit upon a bright idea. He pasted up notices all over the town telling the people that at a certain hour on a certain day he would walk across the river on a rope from one bank to the other. The whole town came to see the stunt, each one paying five kopeks. And sure enough, there was a rope stretched across the river, and out came the acrobat and began to pull up on the rope. Suddenly he stopped and faced his audience.

"Good friends," said he, "I want you to know that I am not a tight-rope walker and if I try to do the stunt, I will surely drown. If, however, it's all right with you that for your five kopeks, a poor Jew should drown in the river, I'll proceed!"

THE REWARD

"Once upon a time," a beggar related, "I came to a rich man's house and I don't know how it happened, but I found myself in the kitchen. In comes the mistress and asks me what I want. 'What shall I want?' I said to her. 'I am a beggar, God help me. Please give me something!' But she—would you believe it?—gave me nothing at all, and scolded me into the bargain. Unheard of *chutzpah*! Then she bangs the door and I am left alone in the kitchen. Imagine, now, how I felt. It was not only that I got nothing, but the insult, you understand, the insult! As soon as I left the house, however, I had my reward. I happened to stick my hand into my pocket, and what do you think I found there? A silver spoon, as I live!"

YOSHKE TRAVELS IN STYLE

Yoshke Ganev was caught riding a horse that didn't belong to him.

"What are you doing on that horse?" he was asked.

Yoshke explained it very simply.

"Last night," he said, "I slept in the house of a peasant, and when I set off early in the morning I found the barnyard locked. Not wishing to awaken my host, I climbed the fence and jumped. And, would you believe it? I landed right on the back of this horse. He was on the other side of the fence, grazing. The animal became frightened and galloped away. And you can see I am telling the truth because —look! He is still galloping!"

YOSHKE IS CURIOUS

Yoshke Ganev was once caught redhanded and brought to trial.

"Your honor," said he to the judge, "will you kindly appoint a lawyer to defend me?"

"Yoshke," said the judge, "you've been caught with the goods, and what could any lawyer say in your defense?"

"Your honor," said Yoshke, "I, too, am curious about it. What could a lawyer say in my defense?"

YOSHKE IS GRATEFUL

After a good beating or a term in prison, Yoshke Ganev used to say:

"I am grateful to the law for beating and hounding those who follow my calling. Were it otherwise, the profession would become overcrowded and it would be impossible to make a living."

MERCY AND LOVE

Yoshke was once haled before a judge who was a convert to the Christian faith. The charge against him was serious, but he denied it.

"Your honor," he ended his plea, "I stand here before you, and I am uncertain whether to appeal to the quality of mercy that lives in your Jewish heart or to the quality of love that lives in your Christian heart!"

TRYING A SCYTHE

"The peasants in our neighborhood," said a merchant, "come to town to buy all sorts of things and they buy very carefully. Take a scythe, for example. A scythe is an important implement and a peasant is in no hurry. He'll try it out. He tries it by throwing it on the ground to see if it has the right ring. He tries it by breathing on it to see if it has the right shine. Then he tries it on his hair to see if it has the right edge. Finally, he tries to steal it."

THE SEEING EYE

A wagon plodded slowly on the country road on both sides of which lay cultivated fields basking in the sunlight of a summer day. In the box of the wagon sat the driver and by his side sat the venerable rabbi who was proceeding to a neighboring town on an important mission. The rabbi's thoughts ran to exalted themes with which the splendor of earth and sky were commingled.

"How wonderful are thy works, O Lord," the rabbi mused.

But the driver thought of other matters, and suddenly he reined in the horse, jumped off the box and cut into a hayfield that stretched along the road. Little mounds of hay lay on the field at regular intervals. The driver approached one of the mounds and looked about him on every side. Then he stooped and gathered up a heap of hay in his arms.

The rabbi was shocked.

"Someone is looking!" he cried.

The driver hastily dropped his pelf and looked about him again on every side. He saw no one. He waited a while, swiftly gathered up again the heap of hay, and threw it into the wagon. Then he mounted the box and whipped up the horses, who raced along the road with all the speed that was in them.

Soon there was a comfortable distance between the driver and the hayfield. He permitted the horses to slow up and turned to his passenger.

"Rabbi," said he, "who was it that you saw looking?"

"The eye that seeth all!" replied the rabbi solemnly. "God!"

The driver gave a deep sigh of relief.

"Oh!" said he, "I thought it was a peasant!"

THINGS THAT VANISH

"We are now coming to a place," said a merchant to his driver, "that is famous for its horse thieves. They are the cleverest horse thieves in the world. When we put up at the inn, you must stay in the wagon without unharnessing and keep watch."

"Trust me, master," said the driver.

The merchant made himself comfortable in the inn, eating and drinking heartily and taking his ease. After a while he stepped outside and called to his driver.

"What are you doing, Berel?" he cried.

"I am sitting and wondering," came the answer.

"Wondering?" asked the merchant.

"Yes, I'm wondering where the hole goes when you've eaten the *baigel*."

"Ah," said the merchant. "Good, very good!"

And he went back to the inn. He sat awhile and becoming uneasy, he stepped out again.

"What are you doing now, Berel?" he called.

"I'm sitting and wondering," said Berel.

"Wondering again?" asked the merchant.

"Yes, I'm wondering where the smoke goes when I light my pipe."

"Good! Very good," said the merchant and returned to the inn.

A little while later, he stepped out a third time.

"What are you doing, Berel?" he cried.

"I'm sitting and wondering," Berel replied.

"Wondering again?" asked the merchant.

"Yes, I'm wondering," said the driver, "where our horses have gone to."

SORROWS OF A THIEF

After being robbed a number of times, a certain householder called in the police who, after examining the premises, noted with surprise that the thief had taken things of negligible worth and left untouched many valuable articles that he could easily have carried away. The police got quickly on the trail of the thief and arrested him. The prisoner was brought before the bar.

"Will you please explain," said the judge, "why you left the valuables behind and stole only a lot of trifles?"

"Please, your honor," the prisoner begged, "don't rub it in. My wife has nagged me enough about it already."

SUGAR

To a well-to-do townsman there once came a *maggid* or *shammes* or some such worthy and was very cordially received. After some small talk, the host asked his guest if he would like some tea and the guest said he wouldn't mind. The tea was brought and thereupon the guest did a strange thing. Instead of taking sugar from the bowl on the table, he dipped into his pocket, took out some lumps of sugar and dropped them into his tea.

"God bless you!" said the astonished host. "Why don't you take sugar from the bowl?"

"*Cholileh!*" said the guest. "I never drink tea with my host's sugar. You see," he went on, "I like a lot of sugar in my tea. I can't impose upon my host, so I always carry sugar with me in my pocket."

The host was compelled to let him have his way. The guest drank a number of glasses of tea and all of them with his own sugar. The time came for him to leave and just before going he did another strange thing. He took the bowl and emptied it into his pocket.

"Mercy on us!" cried the host. "What are you doing? You insisted on drinking my tea with your own sugar, and now you take all my sugar with you!"

"The matter," replied the other, "is very simple. From here I am going to another house and there, too, I will drink tea; from that house to another and so on, and so on. Since I don't drink tea with my host's sugar, where would I take so much sugar? The only thing I can do is what you have just seen. I do it wherever I drink tea because, you understand, I don't like to drink tea with my host's sugar."

MAN AND HORSE

The peasant Mikhail came to town with a load of wood and stopped for a drink in the tavern. Two gentlemen of easy conscience who happened by looked approvingly at Mikhail's horse.

"He looks very good to me," said one. "I propose that we unharness him."

"Not so fast," said the other. "I'm afraid the peasant will catch up with us."

"Leave it to me," replied the first, "we'll unharness the horse and I'll take his place between the shafts."

They did so, and when Mikhail came out of the inn he was dumbfounded to see a man harnessed to his wagon.

"What are you doing here?" he demanded, "and where is my horse?"

"I am your horse," said the man. "Years ago I committed a great sin and for punishment, it was decreed on high that I should be transformed into a horse and labor as a beast of burden until I expiated my sin. This very minute my term expired, and I have changed to my former self."

The peasant was filled with remorse that for so many years he had laid such heavy toil on a human being changed to a horse. He begged the man to forgive him for the many times he had whipped him. Then he released him from the shafts and the man went away.

Several days later, Mikhail came to the same town to visit the fair. He went to the horse mart and recognized his own horse hitched to a post. Mikhail put his arm around the horse's neck and stroked him gently.

"Alas!" said he. "Man is prone to sin. Only a few days ago your expiation ended. Why did you have to go and sin again?"

DOCTOR, LAWYER

MONEY NO OBJECT

The examination over, the patient left two dollars on the table for the doctor.

"My fee," said the eminent specialist, "is ten dollars."

"You see, doctor, I—I'm unable—" the patient began.

"You could have gone to someone cheaper," the doctor interrupted.

"Cheaper?" the patient was surprised. "No, doctor, when it comes to my health money is no object."

SCENE: DOCTOR'S OFFICE

"In there and undress yourself!" said the doctor to the old man who had just entered.

"But, doctor—," the man began.

"I'm too busy to talk to you!" the doctor snapped. "You saw the crowd in my waiting room, didn't you?"

The old man did as he was told. The doctor made a hasty examination.

"I don't understand why you've come here," said he. "You're in perfect health."

"I'm the secretary of the synagogue," the old man explained. "I've come to see you about renewing your membership."

JUST COMMON SENSE

The two patients lay in adjacent beds in the hospital ward, both suffering from the same affliction—a dislocated ankle. The dapper young interne came in and examined the ankle of one of them, turning and twisting it with an impressive professional air. The poor fellow screamed with the pain. The doctor then turned to the other patient. He went through exactly the same procedure, but not a sound escaped from the injured man.

"I admire and envy you," said the first patient to his neighbor when the interne had left. "How can you stand so much pain without a sound?"

"It's not a matter of standing pain," said the other, "it's a matter of common sense."

"What do you mean common sense?" asked the first.

"Do you think," replied the other, "that I was foolish enough to give the young whippersnapper my injured ankle?"

THE MIRACLE

A famous wit fell sick and the doctor who was brought to his bedside shook his head over him.

"There is nothing I can do," said he. "We can only pray for the best."

Several days later the doctor was amazed to see his patient on the street alive and well.

"It's a miracle," said he, "that you've recovered."

"You're mistaken," replied the wit. "It's not true that I've recovered. The fact is that I died. And the miracle happened to you, not me. This is how it came about. As soon as I died and went to heaven, I heard an angel announce: 'All doctors to Hell!' I looked and behold! you were among them. I was taken with a great pity for you. I pleaded with the angel.

" 'Spare this man!' I begged him.

" 'Why?' said the angel. 'Isn't he a doctor?'

" 'No, I can vouch for it!' I cried. 'This man is no doctor!'

"And at once they released you!"

WHAT IS THERE TO SEE?

"You will have to stop drinking or you may lose your eyesight," said the doctor to his patient.

The patient, who was an old man, stood up.

"Doctor," said he, "I have already passed the allotted span of three score and ten and I don't think there is very much that I haven't already seen."

MISTAKE SOMEWHERE

The specialist looked hard at the two dollars which his patient left on the table.

"My fee," said he curtly, "is ten dollars."

"Ten dollars?" the patient repeated. "Somebody told me it was five!"

A GOOD DOCTOR

They were two stammerers and one of them, with great effort, managed to tell the other that his doctor was not doing very much for him.

"Why," said the second stammerer, "d-d-d-don't you g-g-g-go to m-m-m-my d-d-d-d-?"

But that was as far as the poor fellow could go.

A LADY'S AGE

The old lady, who could speak Yiddish only, was being questioned through the court interpreter.

"What is your name?"

"Malke Rabinovitch."

"How old are you?"

She replied and the interpreter translated her answer faithfully:

"Sixty-five till a hundred and twenty."

"What? What's that?" asked the judge. "Did she say she was a hundred and twenty years old?"

"She said: 'Sixty-five till a hundred and twenty,' your honor."

"I don't understand," said the judge. "Repeat the question."

The interpreter repeated the question and again delivered her answer.

"Sixty-five till a hundred and twenty."

His honor felt annoyed.

"What on earth does she mean?" he demanded. "Can't she say how old she is? Ask her again."

And the interpreter translated her answer as follows:

" 'I told you twice already. Sixty-five till a hundred and twenty.' "

His honor mopped his learned brow, and looked bewildered and discouraged.

"Will you permit me, please," said a young lawyer to the interpreter. And turning to the lady, he said to her:

"Grandmother, till a hundred and twenty, how old are you?"

The lady answered and the interpreter translated:

" 'Sixty-five years!' "

INDIAN CHIEF

INDIAN CHIEF

"No," said the skeptic, "I don't think there are any real Indians left. I've made three attempts to find some, and in each case—but let me tell you about them and you'll see what I mean.

"The first place I tried for Indians was Coney Island. There, of course, you expect to find counterfeits, and I saw through them very quickly. I mingled among them and kept my eyes and ears open. Before long, I heard one Indian say to another:

" 'Maybe you have some tobacco, maybe?'

"And the other Indian replied:

" 'Maybe you should start in smoking your own, maybe?'

"There was no mistaking the Brownsville intonation and I had enough.

"The second attempt I made in the middle west. The occasion was a county fair and the Indians were the main attraction. I looked and listened and very soon I became suspicious of the war-whoops. Where, I asked myself, had I heard these sounds before? And suddenly I remembered! They were imitations of the *shofar*-blasts on Rosh Hashanah! I heard them all: *Tekiah, Shevarim, Truah!*

"But once when I was in the far west I made still another attempt. This time I was assured that I would see a famous old Indian chief—the genuine article. I went and paid admission and saw him. Black Turtle sat on a mat, his body as rigid as a stone, looking west with that last-of-the-Mohicans expression. But I refused to be convinced. I waited for him to do something, to talk, to move, to stand up—anything! And finally it happened! The chief stood up grandly and turned around. And I saw something that made me decide never to try again. I was through! Tell me, how would you feel if you saw the *Forverts* sticking out of the back pocket of Black Turtle's trousers?"

HUSBANDS, WIVES, AND CHILDREN

THE MOURNER

In the place of eternal rest a man with bowed head stood over a grave lamenting bitterly. An acquaintance passed by and heard him.

"Why," muttered the unhappy man, "have you gone away never to return? See what you have done to me! See to what you have condemned me!"

As the mourner walked slowly away, the acquaintance approached him.

"I saw you stand over the grave of your first wife," said he.

"No," said the man, "that was the grave of my second wife's first husband."

SHE KNEW HER MAN

"When Adam came home late at night, what was the first thing Eve did?" a certain sage was asked.

"She counted his ribs," the sage replied.

IF NOT NOW, WHEN?

He came to the rabbi and announced that he wanted to divorce his wife.

The rabbi looked up and was surprised: it was an old man who stood before him.

"How long have you been married to your wife?" he asked.

"Forty-five years."

"Are there any children?"

"Three sons and four daughters."

"And where are they?"

"All married."

"And now that you are both old, you want to divorce her?" the rabbi wondered.

"Yes," the man replied, "I want to divorce her. The match was arranged by my father and before the wedding I didn't see her. A few days after the wedding I wanted to divorce her, but my father objected. 'Wait a while and see if she isn't already with child,' said he. She was, and after the child came I wanted to divorce her. 'No,' said my father, 'she's nursing the child.' Then she became pregnant again and had to nurse the second child; then the third, the fourth, the fifth, and so on. Every time I wanted to divorce her, my father, peace unto him, objected. Then she stopped bearing and I wanted to divorce her. 'What are you thinking of?' said my father. 'Do you want your children to grow up motherless?' The children grew up and I wanted to divorce her. 'No,' said my father—and it was just before he died, peace unto him—'it will spoil your children's prospects in marriage!' Now, thank God, they are all married. And if not now, rabbi, when, I ask you?"

"YOUR HUSBAND IS RIGHT!"

The poor woman came to the rabbi and complained that her husband talked of divorcing her.

The old rabbi lifted his brows and looked up from the Talmud over which he was poring.

"Daughter," said he to the woman, "what does your husband say? Has he discovered any fault in you?"

"God forbid!" she replied. "Only he—he says—that I am ugly."

The rabbi began to turn the leaves of his folio.

"He is looking for the law in my case," said the woman to herself. "God grant he may find it to be in my favor."

At last the sage found what he sought: his spectacles. He put them carefully on his nose and looked intently at the woman.

"Daughter," said he, "your husband is right."

THE LOWEST OF THE LOW

"I don't know why it is," said the famous wit, Hershel Ostropoler, "that a woman is held in such light esteem. There are people, I am sorry to say, who consider a woman lower than criminals and apostates! And if you think I am stretching it, I'll tell you what once happened to me.

"I was on my travels and came to an inn that pleased me very much. The place had everything a man of good appetite and good taste could desire. The innkeeper was a wealthy man and he had an only daughter, who, however, was not blessed with beauty. I had a great desire to stay at that inn as long as possible: I had been knocking around a good deal and needed a rest. So I offered to marry the innkeeper's daughter. The man was overjoyed and the virgin was also satisfied. I stayed a few months, ate and drank of the best, and was thoroughly rested.

"The day of the wedding approached and I saw that I must do something. So one day I remarked to the innkeeper:

" 'You know, there are quite a few thieves and felons in my family.'

" 'That's nothing,' said the man and waved the matter aside as though thieves and felons were of no consequence.

"The following day I said to him:

" 'You know, there are also informers and apostates in my family.'

" 'That's nothing at all,' he said.

"Can you imagine it? Informers and apostates meant nothing to him!

"The third day I said to him:

" 'There is a woman in my family—my wife.'

"The man jumped to his feet, cursing and shouting, and drove me out of the inn.

"And there you have it!" Hershel concluded.

MAZEL TOV!

There was a poor man who came to the Free Burial Society and asked them to look after the interment of his wife.

"How's that?" said the president of the society. "We buried your wife two years ago."

"That was my first wife," the man replied. "Now my second wife has died."

"Oh!" said the president, "I didn't know you were married again! Mazel Tov!"

TOO MANY WORDS

The proud young father wired his parents: "Wife bore son—Herman."

His father-in-law took him to task.

"A telegram," said he, "should not have a single unnecessary word. Take, for example, your name, Herman. Why did you have to put that in? Would they think such a message might come to them from anybody at all? Then you say 'wife.' Who else would bear you a son? Some other woman? Then what need is there for the word 'bore'? They know well enough that a child doesn't drop from the sky. Finally, you put in 'son.' Have you ever heard of anyone taking the trouble to wire that his wife gave birth to a daughter?"

AND STILL THEY COME!

"How many little girls have you now?" a poor but resigned father was asked.

"Well," said he, "let's try to figure out. One of them sleeps with my wife and there are two other beds with two apiece. There are the twins who have no bed of their own; they sleep on the floor. In addition, there are the infants. One of them is in the cradle and the other—well, I don't know if the other was born yesterday or is due to arrive to-morrow."

HE PLAYS

"Rabbi," said the unhappy father, "I've just married off my daughter, but she will have to get a divorce. The young man won't do."

"What's wrong with him?" asked the rabbi.

"He can't play cards."

"What? Would to God not a single Jewish young man could play cards!"

"Yes, Rabbi," said the worried father. "But he plays!"

A HAPPY FATHER

"I thank God for my sons," said an elderly man. "My first-born is a doctor. The second is a lawyer, the third a chemist, the fourth an artist, and the fifth a writer."

"And what do you do?" he was asked.

"I," said the man, "have a dry-goods store, not a very big one, but I manage to support them all."

TWO BROTHERS

(*Folk Tale*)

Once there were two brothers, of whom one was very bright and the other very dull. The bright one was famous for his stories and witticisms and wherever he went people welcomed him. The other brother received no attention from anybody and his mother was very unhappy about it.

"Avremele," said she to her bright son. "Have pity on your poor brother. Teach him some of the clever things you know. Teach him an anecdote, a riddle, anything so that people will listen to him."

And Avremele promised, and took his brother aside and taught him.

"Itchikel," said he, "I'll teach you a riddle. You'll go to our neighbor's house and you'll say: 'What am I?' And they'll answer: 'You are a fool and an idiot.' So you'll say: 'Wrong! Guess again!' So they'll say: 'Tell us yourself what you are!' So you'll say: 'I am hungry!' Isn't that smart?"

Itchikel was delighted and he spent the whole day going over and over what his brother had taught him. In the evening he went into the neighbor's house and the house was full of people.

"A riddle!" he cried. "What am I?"

Everybody laughed.

"You are a fool and a donkey," they said.

"Wrong! Guess again!" cried Itchikel.

"Tell us yourself what you are!" the people cried.

"Give me something to eat!" Itchikel answered.

RABBIS AND SCHOLARS

IMPARTIAL

A man from another town once came to a young "modern" rabbi with a strange petition.

"I want you," he said, "to judge between me and the Almighty. I have a number of grievances against Him."

"Why did you come to me?" said the young clergyman. "Isn't there a rabbi in your town?"

"There is," the stranger replied. "But the rabbi in my town is a God-fearing man and I am afraid he will not judge impartially between us. But you, I've been told, have no fear of God, so I know I can trust you."

WHAT FOR THE POOR?

Passover was at hand and the number of families lacking provisions for the festival was greater than usual. The old rabbi of the town determined to visit the well-to-do himself and solicit alms for the needy, and among those he decided to call upon was a certain rich miser, a man of surly and violent temper, whose hand never opened to the poor.

The rabbi lavished all his gifts of persuasion upon the miser without effect. He dilated on the sufferings of the poor, on the beauty and holiness of the Passover festival, on the great rewards of charity, here and in the hereafter. The miser remained obdurate and sullen. The rabbi changed his tone. He became threatening and sarcastic. He spoke of the wrath of God and the contempt of men. He spoke of the penalties reserved for the heartless and greedy in the World-to-Come.

As the miser listened his face became more and more sinister. Finally he jumped up in a rage and struck the rabbi in the face.

For a moment the old man was bewildered. Then his expression lighted up. He turned with a smile to his host.

"This that you have just given me," he said, "was for me. Now what will you give for the poor?"

VENGEANCE AND LOVE

The rabbi and priest were good friends and talked of many things. The priest was an amiable man without religious prejudice, but certain things puzzled him.

"Rabbi," said he once. "You know I'm no anti-semite. But there is something I don't understand. Why do you Jews cling to a God of vengeance? Don't you think you should rather accept the Christian God of love?"

"It's true," said the rabbi, "ours is a God of vengeance, yours is a God of love. I'll not argue with you about it—but what does it all mean? 'Vengeance is mine, saith the Lord.' We leave vengeance to Him, and as for us, we go in for love; as it is written: 'And thou shalt love thy neighbor as thyself.' And if in your case, it is the other way around, are we to blame?"

WHY THE HURRY?

A traveller who had been to the capital returned to his own little town and the rabbi invited him to come and relate the wonders of the great city.

"There is too much to tell," said the returned native, "but something I will tell you. Take for example the electric tramway. If a man has to go from one part of the city to another, he doesn't walk. It would take him too long. He gets on the electric tramway and in a few minutes he arrives. Then there is the railroad. In an hour you go by railroad from one city to another! Now suppose you want to talk to your friend who is a hundred miles away. You have important and urgent business and you must talk to him! Must you go to see him? No. You don't even have to lose time writing letters to him. You take up the telephone and in a few minutes you tell him whatever you wish."

"Wonder of wonders!" said the old rabbi. "But one thing is not clear to me. Why are all the people over there in such a hurry?"

A HEN AND A ROOSTER

Some one came to the rabbi of a small town with a ritual question that baffled him.

"What shall I do?" the man asked. "I have a hen and a rooster and one of them has to go to the pot. But which one? If I take the rooster the hen raises a terrible outcry. She clucks and screams and flaps her wings. If I take the hen, the rooster shrieks so that my blood curdles. What shall I do, rabbi?"

The old rabbi chewed his beard thoughtfully.

"I must look up the law on this matter," said he. "Come back in three days."

"Nu, rabbi?" said the man three days later.

"The law is to take the hen," the rabbi replied.

"But the rooster will protest!" the man cried.

"The rooster will protest?" said the rabbi. "Let him protest!"

TWO BROTHERS

There were two brothers in a town, one of whom was the rabbi and the other the bath-keeper; and the rabbi always snubbed his brother.

"Look here," said the latter one day to the rabbi. "I don't understand why you are so arrogant. If I were like that there would be a good reason for it. My brother is a rabbi! But your brother—what is he? Only a bath-keeper!"

THE *GIMMEL* IN "NOAH"

"Let me ask you a question," said one Talmud student to another.

"Ask," replied the second.

"What need is there for a *gimmel* in 'Noah'?"

"Where do you find a *gimmel* in 'Noah'?"

"Why shouldn't there be a *gimmel* in 'Noah'?"

"What need is there for a *gimmel* in 'Noah'?"

"Eh, but that is *my* question: What need is there for a *gimmel* in 'Noah'?"

LOGIC

After a long session over his Talmud, a scholar stepped out to quench his thirst and returned to resume his study. But first he had to put on his spectacles, and they were gone! He looked for them on the table, he looked for them inside the folio, he looked for them on the floor.

"They are gone!" he declared, and stared helplessly before him.

But the next moment he summoned to his help all his powers of deduction and with the chant of the Talmud to aid him, he reasoned as follows:

"Shall I say that some one came in my absence and took my spectacles? How can I say that? If it was some one who needed spectacles he would have his own. If he didn't need them, why would he take somebody else's? Perhaps I may say that the man was a thief and stole them in order to sell them. But to whom could he sell them? If he offers to sell them to some one who needs spectacles, that person must have spectacles; if to some one who doesn't need spectacles, he won't buy them. I am compelled therefore to conclude that the spectacles were taken by some one who needs spectacles and has spectacles, but he went out in a hurry, moved his spectacles up from his nose to his forehead, forgot that he had done so, and took mine.

"And I'll go further," he continued with renewed zest. "Perhaps I myself am the man who went out in a hurry, and moved his spectacles up from his nose to his forehead and forgot that he did so?"

And thereupon the logician felt his forehead and discovered his spectacles!

"WITH MILK"

From earliest childhood, Rabbi Jonathan of Prague was famous for his phenomenal memory. When he was five years old, a visitor from a distant city asked the boy:

"What is your favorite food?"

"Rice with —," the boy began, but at that moment his father entered, took over the visitor and the conversation ended.

Seven years later the same visitor met Jonathan again.

"With what?" he asked.

"Milk," replied the boy without a moment's hesitation.

WHAT LETTERS!

"Reb Shmerel," said an acquaintance, "what do you hear from your son? What does he write?"

"Thank you very much. Things are not so well with him. His wife died and left him with three small children, such beautiful children! His business is also bad, and it's getting worse all the time. Not long ago he had a robbery and he was left with only his shirt on his back. Things are bad, very bad. But let me tell you something. You should read his letters! It's a pleasure to read them. His style is just marvellous!"

THE LEARNED WAGONER

Yudel has been a wagoner for many years, plying with passengers and freight between his and the neighboring towns. But Yudel is no ordinary *baal-agalah*, not an ignoramus, an *am-ha'aretz* like other wagoners. He is no stranger to the "small print," to the Pentateuch and Rashi, to a chapter of the Psalms; he is even familiar with the famous thirteen principles of Rabbi Ishmael, the thirteen rules for expounding the Holy Writ, such as the rule of *a fortiori* "analogy," etc.

"*Baal-agalah?*" Yudel protested. "I am no *baal-agalah!* I happen to have a horse and wagon and drive from town to town and anyone who cares to join me is welcome. But a *baal-agalah? Cholileh!*"

Now it once happened that Yudel made a long and perilous journey and it was only his learning that saved him and his passengers from disaster. But let Yudel himself tell the story:

"Yes, it was a hard journey, the hardest I ever made. My wagon was overloaded and a fierce storm rose up on the way—a storm of wind and rain and hail, as if Satan the destroyer himself had been given a free hand with the world. And do you want to know what saved us? I can tell you in a word! The principles of Rabbi Ishmael! Just two of them! The rule of *a fortiori* and the rule of analogy. Now you know! And if you want to know it in particular, then listen and you will hear.

"The first prank that Satan played me was to take one of the wheels off the wagon. It fell right off the axle, and what could I do? Immediately I called to my aid the principle of *a fortiori*. 'Since,' I said to myself, 'there are vehicles that roll on only two wheels, my wagon should certainly be able to roll on three.' Soon afterwards, however, I was compelled to invoke the rule of analogy. We hadn't gone far when another wheel fell off! What can a man do when Satan's hand is upon him? 'Since other vehicles run on two wheels,' I argued, 'my wagon can also do it!' And I whipped up my horse and we went on. Before long, however, I had to take refuge again in *a fortiori*. The third wheel fell off the axle! Ah, my friends, where would I now be and where would my passengers be without the blessed *a fortiori*? 'Since,' I said to myself, 'a sleigh moves with no wheels, my wagon should certainly be able to go on one wheel!' And believe me, we would have arrived without further mishap, were it not for Satan who was out to try us to the limit. You guess what I mean: the fourth wheel fell off the axle! 'Oho!' said I, 'so you are at it again, Reb Satan! Well, you may have

the power, but I understand the principle of analogy!'
And at once I reasoned as follows: 'Since a sleigh is
able to proceed without wheels, my wagon can also
do it!' And on we went, and since there were no more
wheels to remove, the Evil One departed from us
and we reached our destination safe and sound!

"Now tell me, I ask you, what would I have done
without *a fortiori* and analogy?"

ANOTHER LEARNED WAGONER

The fate of a certain Jewish community lay in the
hands of the *poretz* who often amused himself by
issuing strange and cruel edicts. But when he proclaimed the edict about the disputation, the community was thrown into a panic. It was to be a debate
between a priest and a Jewish representative. The
debate was to be in the Hebrew language: the priest,
it appeared, was learned in the holy tongue. He
boasted, in fact, that he was more deeply versed in
it than the Jewish scholars.

And this was the way in which the disputation was
to be conducted: the disputants were to ask each
other questions, and woe betide the first who should
be unable to answer! A soldier with a drawn sword
would be stationed near the debaters and the unfortunate man would be immediately beheaded! And
should the Jews fail to send a representative, declared the edict, the entire community, men, women,
and children, would be exiled!

Imagine the despair of the community. Whom

should they send and who would go? If no one went they would all be driven out! If they did send some one they placed him in mortal danger. What if this priest really were as adept as he boasted? On the other hand, was it right for the sake of one to bring disaster upon all?

So they called a solemn assembly to decide whom to send. They waited for some one to volunteer but no one came forward. An atmosphere as of Yom Kippur hung over the gathering. Suddenly a voice made itself heard. It was the voice of Velvel the wagoner.

"Send me," he said, "and I will go!"

What an idea! Everybody knew Velvel to be a complete ignoramus. He could say his daily prayers —without, of course, understanding the meaning— and that was all! How would he stand up before the learned priest? But Velvel insisted.

"Send me," he repeated. "You have no one else. What can you lose?"

There was no alternative. Alas for the wagoner!

The day of the disputation arrived and the place was crowded with people who came from miles around to witness the event. In the center stood the priest and the wagoner, and near them the soldier with the drawn sword. The first question was to be asked by Velvel.

"What is the meaning of *Aineni yodeah*?" asked the wagoner.

"I don't know," replied the priest.

Immediately the soldier acted. He rushed forward and with one blow he beheaded the poor priest.

Velvel was brought back in triumph. The people gathered in the synagogue, said the special prayer of thanks for deliverance from peril, and there was great rejoicing. But everybody was curious. How did the ignorant Velvel think of asking such a shrewd question? Had some one prompted him?

So they asked him to explain and Velvel did so without hesitation.

"The matter," he declared, "is very simple. I once had a teacher who did his best to drive something into my thick head, but it wasn't easy. One day I asked him the meaning of *Aineni yodeah.* 'I don't know,' he replied. Now I remembered that, and when the affair of the disputation came up, I said to myself: 'If my teacher, peace unto him, didn't know, would it be likely that the priest would know?' And sure enough, the priest, thank God, didn't know either!"

PREACHERS AND CANTORS

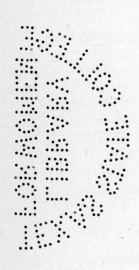

PARABLE OF THE GOAT

The *maggid* of Dubno* was famous for his parables. Arriving in a certain town one day, he stopped at the house of a rich man.

"Welcome!" said the host, "and tell me a nice parable!"

"I'll do so gladly," replied the preacher. "A poor man once bought a goat and when he brought it home, his wife proceeded at once to milk it, but she couldn't obtain a drop. 'This creature,' said she to her husband, 'resembles a goat, but is no goat. There is no milk in her.' To which the man replied: 'This creature is truly a goat and there is milk in her. But she has had a long journey, and is tired and hungry and thirsty. Give her food and drink, and let her rest overnight, and to-morrow she will give you milk.'"

WHAT HAVE I TO DO WITH YOU?

After one of his sermons a certain famous preacher was visited by one of the worthies of the town, a youngish man with advanced ideas, and without beard or earlocks.

"Reb Maggid," said the visitor, "I protest against your sermons. Why do you frighten our people with

* Jacob Krantz (1741-1804).

177

your old wives' tales? Why don't you leave out those lurid pictures of Hell and its demons?"

The *maggid* was taken aback but he recovered quickly and spoke to his visitor as follows:

"Let me tell you something that once happened to me. I was on my travels one day when I met an ox. The ox stopped and extended a hoof in greeting.

" '*Sholem aleichem!*' said the ox.

" 'Foolish beast,' said I, 'what have I to do with you?'

" 'You eat of my flesh,' the ox replied; and recognizing the justice of his reply, I returned his greeting.

"I proceeded on my way and met a cow. The animal stopped and greeted me.

" '*Sholem aleichem!*' said the cow and held up one of her hoofs.

" 'Silly cow,' said I, 'what have I to do with you?'

" 'You drink my milk,' the cow replied. I had to admit the truth of what she said and returned her greeting.

"I went on and before long I met a goat. The goat took his stand in front of me, shook his head solemnly, and greeted me.

" '*Sholem aleichem,*' said the goat and lifted one of his forelegs.

" 'Ridiculous beast,' said I, 'what have I to do with you?'

"The goat nodded to me and replied:

" 'Look, I have a beard and so have you!'

" 'You are right,' said I and returned his greeting.

"Finally I met a pig and the pig also lifted a leg and greeted me. I became very angry.

"'Loathsome beast!' I cried. 'Your flesh I don't eat, your milk I don't drink, of a beard you have no vestige! What on earth have I to do with you?'"

SUCH IS LIFE!

"A human being," said a preacher in a mood of pessimism, "may be compared to a ladies' tailor. A ladies' tailor goes on living till he dies and the same is true of a human being."

FOR SELF-CONFIDENCE

He was a famous preacher and the town to which he came received him gladly. The evening before his first sermon he visited the richest man in town and asked for a loan of ten rubles.

"I'll return the money immediately after my sermon," he promised.

The rich man hesitated, but finally granted the loan.

The preacher kept his promise. His sermon pleased the people and he was invited to preach again and again. And always before each sermon, he borrowed ten rubles from the rich man and after the sermon returned the loan.

The rich man was puzzled.

"I don't understand you," said he to the preacher finally. "If you need the money, why do you return it without using it? If you don't need the money, why do you borrow it?"

"My friend," the preacher explained, "do you realize what self-confidence it gives a man who is facing an audience when he has ten rubles in his pocket?"

A CASE OF JUSTICE

The preacher stood and held forth in his best manner, but a loud snore was heard in the audience. The preacher stopped and called the *shammes*.

"Will you please wake up that man?" said he.

"It's not fair," said the *shammes*, "you put him to sleep, you wake him up!"

THE KEY

The preacher stood on the platform and gave his audience all he had, but to no avail. One by one, his hearers arose and left the synagogue. Finally only the sexton and the preacher remained.

Timidly the sexton approached the preacher and handed him a key.

"When you are through," he whispered, "will you be kind enough to lock the synagogue?"

GRATEFUL

One Sabbath afternoon an itinerant preacher held forth in the synagogue and the following day, in accordance with custom, he went from house to house to collect his honorarium. One of the worthies of the town received him with special cordiality and gave him a handsome gratuity. The preacher was delighted.

"So you liked my sermon!" he smiled.

"Well," the other replied, "it's not exactly that. For a long time I've been suffering from insomnia, but as soon as you began I fell asleep and slept right through to the end."

HE WANTS TO KNOW

For time out of memory it has been the custom of cantors to place their thumbs under their chins when scaling into the higher octaves. And once a young admirer asked a certain famous cantor:

"Why do you do that?"

"I've been doing it for fifty years without knowing why," the cantor replied, "and now comes a whipper-snapper like you and wants to know!"

HOW IT HAPPENED

For reasons good or bad, cantors have always been the victims of scoffers and wags, and the following legend is not the worst of the jibes that have been directed against them:

At the time of Creation, every living creature, so it was decreed, was to be allotted a life-span of forty years. Whereupon the horse appeared and asked to know what his destiny would be on earth.

"Men will ride on your back," he was told.

"In that case," the horse replied, "twenty years will be enough for me."

Then came the donkey and asked the same question.

"You," he was told, "will be made to bear heavy burdens."

"In that case," said the donkey, "I'll be satisfied with twenty years."

After the donkey came the cantor.

"What am I destined to do on earth?" he asked.

"Your work," he was told, "will be most pleasant. You will do nothing but sing hymns and praises."

"In that case," said the cantor, "I would like my life-span to be doubled."

Whereupon a solemn council was held in heaven and it was decided to take away twenty years from the horse and twenty from the donkey, and add them to the life-span of the cantor.

It was so ordered; and that is why a cantor sings as he should during the first forty years of his life. The next twenty years he neighs like a horse, and the next twenty he brays like a donkey.

THE OIL WOULD HAVE FLOWED ON

This is a story about an ambitious cantor and an accommodating rabbi. It came to the cantor's ears that the neighboring community was looking for a cantor and he resolved to apply for the position, so he went to his rabbi and spoke as follows:

"The neighboring community is larger and richer, and it's time that I got on in the world. Help me to get the position. Give me your recommendation."

Now the rabbi who, of course, knew the cantor well, pondered the matter a long time, but finally gave him a paper on which was written the following:

"If the holder of this note had been living in the days of the Prophet Elisha, the oil would not have stopped flowing."

The cantor took the note to the neighboring town where it was read by the town worthies who, although they were rather mystified by it, were also impressed.

"This man," said they, "must be no ordinary cantor, or the rabbi would not write about him in that way."

So they engaged the applicant and it was not many weeks before they discovered the truth. They discovered, indeed, that their cantor was an incompetent, an ignoramus, and a fool to boot! But they had to put up with him, for what could they do? Nevertheless, they harbored a deep grudge against the rabbi. What did he mean by saying such things about a good-for-nothing?

And it came to pass that one of the worthies visited the neighboring town and determined to call on the rabbi and ask for an explanation. He found the sage seated in his study, bent over his Talmud folio, and the visitor respectfully but firmly explained his errand.

"My son," replied the rabbi, "read over again the

fourth chapter of the Second Book of Kings. It's the story of the oil that flowed miraculously on. Now why did the flow cease? Because there was not one empty vessel left. It follows therefore that if that captor had been present the oil would have flowed on."

BUYERS, SELLERS, AND BORROWERS

A FOX-TERRIER

The Polish squire summoned his Jewish purchasing agent.

"Yankel," said he, "my wife has made me promise I would get her a fox-terrier. Will you go out and buy me one? And remember, I want a good one!"

"Of course, Your Excellency! At once!" the agent replied. "And how much is Your Excellency willing to pay for a good fox-terrier?"

"Fifty crowns," said the squire.

"Impossible, Your Excellency," said Yankel.

"How much, then?"

"At least a hundred."

"A hundred crowns?"

"At least, Your Excellency."

"Well—all right. A hundred then. But hurry up!"

But Yankel stood still.

"Why don't you go?" the Pan demanded.

"Your Excellency. . . ."

"Yes?"

"Tell me, I beg of you, what is a fox-terrier?"

NO PROFIT, NO LOSS

"Shimshon," said Motel the clothing dealer, "you are my *landsman* and I'll sell you a suit that you'll

187

thank me for all your life. And cheap, do you hear? Why should I make money on you? You're my *landsman!* Here is the suit, the best in the store! And will I ask you sixty dollars for it, which it is worth? Oh, no! Not sixty, and not fifty and not even forty. Thirty dollars is all you will pay me. Take it, it's yours!"

"Motel," said Shimshon, "I can't see you should lose money on me. Why should you lose on me? You are my *landsman!* So what will I offer you for this suit? Will I offer you six dollars? Oh, no! I will not offer you so little, and not even eight dollars or ten dollars. Motel, I'll give you twelve dollars for that suit, not a cent less!"

"It's yours, Shimshon," said Motel.

WELL-STOCKED

The customer bought a cigar, lighted it, took a few puffs and returned to the tobacconist.

"I asked you for a good cigar," he cried, "and you give me this stinker!"

The man looked sadly at his customer and said nothing.

"Why don't you say something?" the customer demanded.

"What can I say?" replied the tobacconist. "I'm thinking what a lucky man you are. You have only one of those cigars, but my store is just full of them."

THEY AGONIZE!

"Dear friend," wrote a merchant to one of his creditors, "I have settled in a new place and opened a business that cannot fail. I carry two lines: bread and shrouds. People, you know, either live or die. If they live, they need bread; if they die, they need shrouds. The money I owe you is virtually in your pocket. In three months you'll hear from me."

Three months passed, and three more.

"Nu?" wrote the creditor to the merchant.

"My friend," the merchant replied, "this is a strange place where I have settled. The people here neither live nor die. They just agonize."

LOANS AND HOT DOGS

The hot dog merchant stood with his little stand on the sidewalk near the bank. Along came a *landsman*.

"How is business?" asked the *landsman*.

"Not bad," replied the merchant. "I have already put away some savings in the bank, thank God."

"In that case," said the *landsman*, "can you lend me five dollars?"

"God forbid!" replied the merchant. "I have no right to do it!"

"What do you mean you have no right?" the other inquired.

"You see," the merchant replied, "I have an agreement with the bank that we are not to interfere with each other. I am forbidden to make loans and the bank is forbidden to sell hot dogs."

"IT'S A LIE"

They were discussing the latest gadgets in the art of book-keeping.

"It's all nonsense!" said one. "My grandfather, peace unto him, was ignorant of the art, but he never made a mistake in his accounts."

"How did he do it?" he was asked.

"Very simply. He had a little book where he kept a record of all his transactions. Suppose he gave someone a loan of fifty cents. He'd write down: 'Seventh day of Nissan: So-and-so owes me fifty cents.' When so-and-so paid, my grandfather wrote: 'The above statement that so-and-so owes me fifty cents is a lie!'"

DEBTOR AND CREDITOR

"When will you pay me what you owe me?" Yankel asked his friend Berel.

"What do you think I am?" Berel answered. "A fortune teller?"

So Yankel took his creditor to the rabbi.

"Rabbi," said Yankel, "this man owes me money and doesn't pay."

"Rabbi," said Berel, "this month I am hard pressed and I cannot pay."

"Didn't you say the same thing last month?" Yankel demanded.

"Well," cried Berel, "did I pay you last month?"

A MASTER-CRAFTSMAN

The rich man ordered a new suit of clothes for his son's wedding.

"See that you make a good job," said he to the tailor. "You know the people of this town. If anything isn't just so, they will make merry over it."

"Don't worry," replied the tailor. "I've been practicing my trade now for thirty years, and it hasn't happened yet that people should make merry over my work. On the contrary, they always weep over it."

MORE THAN THE ORDER

The traveling salesman came to a customer and inquired if there was a telegram for him.

"Here it is," said the customer.

The salesman opened it and his face fell.

"My wife," he said sadly, "has presented me with twins."

"Good!" cried the customer. "Now you'll know how it feels to receive more goods than you order."

RED WINE AND WHITE

The wine salesman insisted on the superior quality of his red wine.

"But I am stocked up on red wine," the customer pleaded, "I don't want any."

"My red wine," the salesman began and he went off on another eulogy. Finally the customer lost his temper. He took the salesman by the collar and threw him out.

An hour later the salesman returned.

"What happened an hour ago," said he to the customer, "was in connection with red wine. Now what about white wine?"

MARRIAGE BROKERS AND OTHER LIARS

HE HAS THEM ALL

"Young man," said a *shadchen*, "I have an excellent match for you; the girl is a beauty."

To which the young man replied: "Please, don't bother me."

"Very well," the *shadchen* continued, "if beauty is not the main thing with you, I have another one, not so beautiful, but not homely either, and she has five thousand rubles."

And again the young man replied: "Please, don't bother me."

"So!" continued the *shadchen*. "I see your standards are very high. Well, I have one for you with twenty thousand."

"Don't bother me," said the young man. "Money is not my object."

"No?" said the *shadchen*. "Is it *yichus*? Well, I have some one for you of the finest family. Ten generations of rabbis!"

"I want you to know," said the young man with finality, "that I am not interested in any of your proposals. I will marry for love only."

"Oh, I see!" said the *shadchen*. "Well, I have one like that also!"

JUST A LITTLE BIT

"I want you to know," said Shaye Shadchen to one young man, "that I am a man of truth. I never misrepresent. I never exaggerate. If anything is not quite the way it should be, I inform my clients in advance. Now in the case of this young lady that I am advising you to marry, she is qualified for you in every respect. She is beautiful, she is educated, she comes of good family, and she brings a good dowry. But she has one fault. She is just a little bit pregnant."

ONE-EYED, BUT—

There was a wealthy man in town who was anxious to marry off his daughter and to him came Shaye Shadchen and proposed a certain young man whom the marriage-broker declared eligible on every count. Shaye praised the young man to the skies and the father wanted to meet him.

"There is one thing I must tell you beforehand," said Shaye who knew when to reveal a thing and when to conceal it. "The young man possesses sight in only one eye."

"You mean he is blind in one eye?" asked the astonished father.

"Yes, I must admit it," said Shaye, "but—"

But the father cut him short.

"I'm surprised at you," said he, "that you know

no better than to propose a one-eyed husband for my daughter!"

"What's wrong with that?" Shaye demanded. "Do you know that the author of the great book 'Menorath Hamoar'* was blind in one eye?"

"And not only that," continued the aggrieved father, "but that young man, you admit, is very poor."

Shaye became indignant in his turn.

"Who is more illustrious than the famed poet and philosopher Abraham Ibn Ezra?"* he demanded. "And yet Abraham Ibn Ezra was a pauper!"

The father jumped to his feet.

"But this young man is an ignoramus!" he cried.

Shaye Shadchen smiled at the man benevolently. He took a pinch of snuff and held out the box to his client.

"Do you find that Rothschild is such a learned man?" he asked.

IRRESISTIBLE!

Shaye Shadchen called on a certain young man who was somewhat infected with modern ideas. The young man gave him a cold reception.

"I think," said he, "I have told you already that I shall marry a girl with whom I fall in love and none other."

"That's exactly why I have come!" said Shaye. "Listen! Five thousand rubles down! The father is seventy years old, as rich as Korah, and she is his

* See Glossary.

only child. And that's not all! She has an old uncle who is also very rich and childless! I ask you now, is it possible not to fall in love with a girl like that?"

IT'S OVER AND DONE!

With another young man Shaye Shadchen struggled valiantly for a long time until every difficulty seemed to have been removed. In the end the prospective groom discovered that the bride limped, and he called the whole thing off.

"I'll not have a lame wife, if she had the wealth of Korah!" he declared.

Whereupon Shaye Shadchen spoke to the young man as follows:

"Let us assume, my young friend, that you take a woman after your own heart and that both her legs are strong and sound. Are you sure that some day or other she won't slip and break one of them? She'll be laid up for weeks and months, you'll ruin your health with watching and worrying, and become impoverished in the bargain! Now take that girl! She has already broken her leg, she has been cured by others, and with other people's money. It has all been done for you; you have nothing more to worry about!"

NO ONE IS PERFECT

There was another young man in town to whom Shaye spoke at length on the bride's dowry.

"Remember," said he, "five thousand down, besides jewels and precious stones, and a trousseau, such a trousseau on every Jewish daughter!"

"But," said the young man, "she limps a little, doesn't she?"

"And what if she does?" said Shaye. "Do you suppose she can't afford a carriage?"

"And her eyes, I understand, are rather weak," the young man added.

"The better for you," said Shaye, "she won't see your faults."

"And besides that, she stammers," the young man continued.

"Lucky man!" said Shaye. "Would you have a wife that would talk your head off?"

"But—but," said the young man, "what about that —that hump on her back?"

"God in heaven!" cried Shaye, jumping to his feet, "Do you want her to be perfect?"

FOUR MORE DAUGHTERS

Shaye Shadchen likes to tell the following story as illustrating the difficulties to be encountered in his profession:

"The bride's father accepted the terms and everything was ready for the betrothal. The last minute he takes me aside and says:

" 'The groom insists on two thousand, and more than a thousand I can not—'

"I knew my man and interrupted him.

" 'And even a thousand,' I said, 'are you in a position to—'

" 'No, of course not,' he replies, 'but a thousand I could promise.'

" 'And not pay,' I added.

" 'No, of course not,' he admitted.

" 'In that case,' said I, 'why can't you promise two thousand and not pay?'

" 'What are you thinking of?' says my man. 'Don't you know I have four more daughters?' "

HE ASKS TO BE REMEMBERED

When it was all over and the couple was happily married, Shaye Shadchen approached the bride and whispered in her ear.

"Mazel-tov!" said he.

"Mazel-tov!" replied the beaming bride.

"I have a little favor to ask of you," said Shaye.

"What is it?" asked the bride.

"My name is Shaye. I want you to remember my name. Shaye."

"I shall remember your name all my life, Reb Shaye," replied the bride and smiled happily. "But why do you make this request of me?"

"Because," said Shaye, "in later years I don't want you to say it was the devil who brought you to this pass."

SHAYE DEMANDS A FEE

There was a wealthy man in town who found a satisfactory match for his daughter, but not with the help of Shaye Shadchen.

The day after the wedding, Shaye appeared and claimed a fee.

"Have you gone out of your mind?" asked the man.

"No, my friend," said Shaye, "but I'm a *shadchen.*"

"But I got my son-in-law through another *shadchen!*" the man protested.

"That's exactly why you should pay me a fee," said Shaye. "You should do it out of simple gratitude. You see," he whispered in the man's ear, "not one of the marriages I ever arranged has endured."

THE RIGHT DAY

There was a certain young man who was neither handsome, nor rich, nor learned—a very ordinary young man. One day, a *shadchen* called on him and proposed an extraordinary match.

"The father is one of the richest men in town," he said. "The young lady is highly educated and beautiful."

"Then why—," began the young man who was not altogether a fool.

But a *shadchen* knows in advance what a client intends to say.

"Why they would favor you?" said the *shadchen.*

"Let me tell you the whole truth. Every half year the young lady goes insane. Her insanity lasts only a day, and she is well again for another half year."

The young man thought the matter over. Only two days a year—it's not so terrible! One can put up with it.

"Very well," said he to the *shadchen,* "we'll go and see the bride."

"Not to-day," the *shadchen* replied. "We must wait a few months for the day when she is out of her mind."

NOODLES WITH MILK

He was a simple village lad, and the marriage-broker, after arranging the preliminaries, took him to the neighboring town to be introduced to the prospective bride.

On the way the *shadchen* instructed him on proper manners and conversation.

"Remember," he told him, "there are three subjects that women like to talk about: family affairs, good things to eat, and clever sayings."

The young man promised to remember.

"Have you any brothers or sisters?" he asked the maiden, beginning with subject number one.

"No," she replied, "I am an only child."

There was a pause and the village lad decided to proceed to the next subject.

"Do you like noodles with milk?" said he.

"No," replied the maiden, "I don't like noodles with milk."

There was another pause and the young man felt it was time for the third subject. He thought hard and finally said:

"If you had brothers and sisters, would you like noodles with milk?"

CAN'T WAIT

There was a *shadchen* whose wife gave him no peace.

"You are providing husbands for all the girls in town," she nagged him, "and our own Malkele is becoming an old maid!"

But what could the poor *shadchen* do? The young men were insisting on a handsome dowry, and where was he to find it? Nevertheless his wife's nagging had its effect and one day he went to the rich man of the town to propose a match for his daughter.

"Reb *Shadchen*," said the rich man, "what's the hurry? My daughter is only fifteen years old. She can wait!"

"Yes," replied the *shadchen*, "but my daughter can't! She is over thirty."

WOLVES!

Zavel Liar's specialty was wolves. His experiences with wolves were hair-raising.

"Once when I was in the forest alone," he narrated, "I was attacked by ninety-nine wolves."

"Exactly ninety-nine?" objected one of his listeners. "Why not a hundred?"

"Well," said Zavel, "perhaps there were a hundred, but I don't like to exaggerate."

On another occasion, however, Zavel made it a hundred.

"Exactly a hundred?" he was asked. "Were you able to count them?"

"Well," said Zavel, "if there weren't a hundred, there were certainly fifty."

"Perhaps there were twenty," some one suggested. Zavel was a little offended.

"Why must you quibble about it?" he said. "A single wolf is also dangerous!"

"But did you see the wolf with your own eyes?" another insisted.

Now Zavel was really hurt.

"What do you think it was," he demanded, "that made that noise in the bushes?"

FISH FOR THE FEAST

"So you don't believe in miracles!" said an old-timer. "Well, listen to what I'll tell you, and see what you can make of it. I was on my travels one cold winter day, and I was crossing a frozen river to get to a village on the other side. Suddenly the ice broke under me and I fell into the water. I shouted for help and some peasants came running and pulled me out. When I stood up I was a pillar of ice and my beard was frozen solid. The peasants took me to a Jewish house and I found the place full of people: they were celebrating a wedding. But the host was sad and forlorn: he had been unable to obtain fish for the feast.

"In the meantime, I was beginning to thaw out. They put me into a barrel, and the water ran in torrents from my body and my beard. And what do you think happened? Two good-sized fishes, a carp and a yellow-pike, leaped out of my beard and flapped right into the barrel. I leave you to imagine the joy of my host and all his guests!"

AND A WALL-CLOCK!

"Or consider this incident," the old-timer continued. "It was the day before Passover and in my house poverty reigned like a king. There was no vestige of anything: no matzo, no wine, no eggs—nothing! The wife is in tears, the children are scared, and as for me, what could I do? I went to the market-place. I took my stand near a large store and stood wondering whence my salvation would come. A cab pulls up near the store, and my heart goes pit-apat! A lady steps out of the cab, arranges her satin dress, takes out her silk handkerchief and a bundle falls out of it right at my feet! 'Oh Lord!' I prayed, 'send me salvation!' And God heard my prayers. I picked up the bundle and opened it. It contained thirty rubles in copper and in addition, guess what! A wall-clock, as I live!"

LUXURY—AND CHEAP

The man from Vilna and the man from Odessa were praising their own cities, and each of them was running down the city of the other.

"Vilna," said the man from Odessa, "is no place to live in. All you have to eat there is black bread and cucumbers, and even that comes high. And what do you drink? Nothing but water. But in Odessa, we live in luxury. We eat and drink of the best, and everything is dirt cheap. You can get a five pound fish for a kopek and a gallon of wine for five kopeks."

The man from Vilna was roused.

"It's a lie!" he declared.

"A lie, did you say?" replied the man from Odessa. "Very well then, it's a lie. But a kopek for a five pound fish and five kopeks for a gallon of wine is cheap enough, isn't it?"

SOME SLIGHT CORRECTIONS

"In Odessa," the man continued, "nothing is too good for us. Take the cantor of our great synagogue, for example. The man's throat is like a musical instrument, David's harp! He costs us enough, you may be sure—twenty thousand rubles a year! His name, by the way, is Marcus."

"Twenty thousand a year!" some one objected. "Impossible!"

"Don't say that," interrupted the man from Vilna. "I can vouch for that, except for a few minor details. First, the city is not Odessa, but Kiev, and the man's name is not Marcus but Brodsky. Further, he is not a cantor but a lumber merchant, and instead of making twenty thousand a year, he loses thirty. Everything else is correct."

A TALL ONE

"People talk about high mountains. But if you want to hear about a really high mountain, listen to me. I happen to be a merchant, you must know, and my line of business is geese. Yes, I buy and sell geese, flocks of them! And it happened once that I had to take a flock of geese from one place to another and between the two stood a mountain, the very mountain I want to tell you about. Well, we started, my geese and I, up the mountain, the geese in front and I behind, urging them on. We climbed and climbed and, how long, do you think, did it take us to reach the summit? You'll never guess! Two and a half years, as true as you are looking at me! Well, we got to the top and, naturally, by that time the geese were hungry. But I had nothing to give them. The geese, like all birds of their species, began to peck. Now what, I ask you, did they peck at? Corn? Oats? Berries? No, my friend, the stars, that's what they pecked at, the stars, as true as I am talking to you! So there you are, if you want to know something about high mountains!"

SNOW

"Since you talk about snow, I am reminded of a sleigh-ride a number of us took many years ago. Listen and you'll hear something. The sleigh was not large, we had but one horse, and we started out in high spirits. We were young, you understand! We came to an elevation and by the time we got to the top of it, it was midday and we were hungry. So we ate, and after eating we felt drowsy. We unharnessed the horse and tied him to a pole that stuck up out of the snow. Then we turned the sleigh upside down, stretched out, and fell asleep. The day was not cold; the sun, in fact, was warm, and we were quite comfortable. When we woke up, we looked around and what do you think! The snow was gone. The sleigh was resting on green grass. So we knew that the sun had melted the snow while we slept. We looked for the horse and the horse too was gone! Where could the horse be? How were we going to get back without the horse? We look here, we look there, no horse! Finally I happen to look up, and there was our horse dangling from the steeple of a church! Now figure out how high that snowdrift was where we had stopped to rest."

THE LION

"Men talk about strength and they talk about wisdom. Which of the two, you ask, is more to be

desired? Wisdom, of course! Everybody knows that
our people have chosen wisdom, that we are the
wisest people on earth! Nevertheless, there are times
when strength is also important. What, for example,
would I have done on certain occasions if it were
not for my unusual strength? Listen and judge for
yourself. I was on my way through a forest when I
met a lion. Have you ever met a lion in a forest?
No? Don't laugh—it's no laughing matter. The lion
roared and rushed right at me, his jaws wide open!
Was I frightened? I don't deny that I was—a little.
But the next moment I laughed at him. I remembered how strong I was! So what did I do? I plunged
my arm right between his jaws! I plunged it deeper
and deeper until I came to his tail. I seized his tail
and with one powerful wrench I pulled the lion inside out! Then I swung him by the tail over my
shoulder and brought him home. Thus I was delivered from great danger and in addition, my wife,
God bless her, and I had fur coats for the winter,
which, that year, was very severe. Shall I tell you
about the frosts we had that winter? No? Very well,
some other time!"

WEDDING-GUESTS

A great event was in the offing for the little town:
the rich man of the place was marrying off his
daughter—his youngest daughter! It was to be a
wedding such as the town had never had before.

Everybody was to be there, young and old, rich and poor, men, women, and children.

But as the day approached, the bride's father became worried. The whole town, he learned, was preparing to come! That, he thought, would be too much. Such a throng he was unwilling to receive, or perhaps he was unable to do it! You can't be too sure about your rich men these days! So he instructed the butler to admit only those who had something to do with the preparations for the wedding or could show a relationship to the families, either his or the groom's.

The butler hired two yokels, put them into uniforms, and stationed them near the entrance, having first told them what they must do. The people began to arrive, streams of them, and the yokels asked them who they were. Said one:

"I am a brother-in-law of the bride's uncle's grandmother."

"Enter!" said the yokels.

"I am a cousin of the man you have just admitted," said the next.

"Certainly! Step inside," said the yokels.

"I am the man who grated the horse-radish for the wedding," said another.

"The horse-radish? Inside!"

"My grandfather's father-in-law officiated at the circumcision of the bridegroom's great aunt's son."

"Indeed! Step inside, please!"

"I am the man who pounded the pepper."

"Enter!"

And hard upon the last, came some one whom no one had ever seen before.

"Who are you?" asked the yokels.

"I am the pepper-pounder's son-in-law."

"Enter!" said the yokels in uniform.

And when the rich man looked out upon his guests, it seemed to him that the whole town was there after all.

GLUTTONS, GUZZLERS AND OTHER SINNERS

WHAT A GLUTTON!

When he got to the village, the traveler, hungry and tired, stepped into the inn and sat down at a table.

"What will you have?" asked the innkeeper's wife.

"Soup and meat," said the traveler.

"Sorry," said the woman, "we have meat only on Sabbath."

"Some fish then," said the hungry man.

"No fish," she replied, "we have no river in this village."

"Then bring me some milk and cheese."

"We haven't any," said the woman, "the cows around here have stopped giving milk."

"How about a herring?" asked the traveler finally.

"It's not here yet. My husband hasn't come back from town."

"Some bread then?" cried the traveler. "Can you give me a piece of bread?"

The woman turned and walked away.

"I never saw such a glutton in all my life!" she muttered.

NO NEWS

A stranger sat down at a table in the town tavern, and ordered fish. When the waiter brought it, the stranger examined it closely, then bent down over the plate and began to whisper. The other customers looked on with amazement. The stranger continued to whisper to the fish, and, between whispers, he seemed to listen. Finally the proprietor approached the man.

"What are you doing?" he demanded.

"I'm having a little chat with the fish," said the stranger. "I said: 'How do you do?' and they answered: 'Thank you. How are you?' I said: 'How is it down in your world?' 'Pretty good,' said they, 'sorry we had to leave it.' 'Where do you come from?' I asked them. 'From a river not far from here,' they told me. 'And what's the latest news down in your river?' I asked them. 'News?' they answered. 'Don't ask us. It's more than month now since we left the place!'"

ANOTHER PORTION OF PUDDING!

A young modern was observing the anniversary of his father's death, and in keeping with the occasion, he went to a kosher restaurant. It was a Saturday and the menu included a delicious Sabbath pudding. The young man finished his portion and a wave of filial emotion swept over him.

"Waiter!" he called, "bring me another portion of pudding! My father deserves it!"

CAUSE FOR REJOICING

On the festival of "Joy in Torah," the tippler, even while he danced and drank, was heard to chant the well-known words: "Man's origin is dust and his end is dust."

"What sort of words are those for a joyous day like this?" someone protested.

"They are the right words," the tippler replied. "If man's origin were gold and his end dust, he would have reason for regret. But if his origin is dust and his end is dust, and he manages in between to empty a bottle or two, why shouldn't he rejoice?"

NO MATTER WHEN

Before lying down for his afternoon nap, a certain tippler refreshed his spirits and said to his wife:

"Woman, wake me up as soon as I get thirsty."

"What kind of nonsense is that?" said the woman. "How will I know when you are thirsty?"

"It doesn't matter," the man replied, "whenever you wake me up, I'll be thirsty."

A QUESTION OF DATE

After consulting the doctor, a certain old guzzler met a friend.

"What did he tell you?" asked the friend.

"He told me I must stop drinking. It's a question of life and death."

The two walked on in silence. As they passed the tavern, the sick man turned and went inside. He ordered a tall glass of liquor and brought it down at a gulp.

"Are you tired of living?" asked his friend.

"Not exactly," replied the other. "I'm only assuming that I saw the doctor tomorrow instead of today."

THE RIDDLE

(Folk Story)

"Yoshek," said one peasant to another, "we've sat together for three hours, drinking all the time. But I don't feel so happy. How about you?"

Yoshek laid his head on his arm and groaned.

"No, Stepan," he replied, "I don't feel happy either."

"Listen, Yoshek!" Stepan continued, "I hear the Jews tell each other a lot of funny stories. They tell riddles and things that make you laugh. Go to their synagogue, Yoshek, little brother. Stand near the windows and listen, and bring back a good story or a riddle. I want to laugh, Yoshek, do you hear? I must laugh!"

And Yoshek staggered out and made his way to the synagogue and stood near an open window. In-

side a group of men sat together and gossiped. Said
one of them, who had a long red beard:

"Guess this one: my parents have a son, but I have
no brother. Who is it?"

"It's yourself!" a number of voices replied.

Yoshek laughed and staggered back to his friend.

"Stepan, dear little brother," he said, "guess this
one: my parents have a son, but I have no brother.
Who is it?"

Stepan looked at Yoshek long and mournfully.
But he found nothing to say.

"Stepan, little brother," said Yoshek at last. "You're
stupid. It's the Jew with the long red beard in the
synagogue!"

And Yoshek and Stepan laughed uproariously together, embracing each other and slapping each other
on the back, until they rolled together under the
table.

NOT CRAZY FOR THE STUFF

"Rifkele," said a husband to his wife, "I am not
feeling so well. It must be the cucumbers I ate. Is
there a drop of brandy in the house?"

It was in the dead of night and the woman was
fast asleep, but the matter was important and the
man didn't hesitate to wake her.

"Brandy?" she repeated in a loud angry whisper.
"In the middle of the night he has to have brandy!
Go to sleep! There's no brandy in the house!"

"If you think I'm crazy for the stuff, you're mistaken," said the man resignedly and turned his face to the wall.

It was not long, however, before he called her again.

"Rifkele," said he, "our neighbor always has some in his house. Couldn't you get me a drop from him? I don't feel so well."

"Have you gone crazy?" said the woman. "What kind of idea is it to go knocking on people's doors at this time of the night for liquor? Go to sleep! You'll feel better in the morning."

"All right!" said the man. "Only I don't want you to think I'm crazy for the stuff."

But soon enough he called her again.

"Rifkele," said he, "I have just remembered. To-morrow there is a fair in town and the peasants arrive during the night. The tavern must be open already. Couldn't you run down and get me a little glass of brandy?"

But now the woman was in a rage.

"May all the evil dreams I dreamt this night and every other night descend on your head!" she cried. "Guzzler! Drunkard! In the middle of the night, in a bitter frost, I should go and get him brandy!"

"Hush!" the man whispered, "you'll wake up the children! Do you think I'm crazy for the stuff? Only if you don't care to go, I'll get up and go myself."

FORGOT HIS MAKER

The ignorant village inn-keeper lived all year round among the peasants, far removed from the people of his faith, and once when he came to town for the High Holy Days, the rabbi spoke harsh words to him. The man stood before the rabbi ashamed and confused.

"It wouldn't surprise me," said the rabbi, "if you don't even know who made you!"

"It's true, rabbi," the man confessed, "I don't know."

The rabbi turned to a small boy who stood near.

"Tell me, son," he asked him, "who made you?"

"God!" the youngster replied promptly.

The rabbi turned again to the villager.

"The child," he declared, "knows more than you!"

"I know why," the inn-keeper ventured. "He was born not so long ago and still remembers. But how can I remember so many years back?"

CARD SHARPS

In a tavern sat two worthies, eyeing sharply all who came and went. They were of dubious appearance and restless demeanor. They were, in fact, looking for some one whom they might persuade to join them in a game of cards. But there finally remained only one other person in the room, an elderly man of dignified appearance who did not look like very promising quarry. Having no choice, however, they approached the man and asked him if he would join them in a game.

"Eh, what?" said the elderly man. "A little louder, please!"

The invitation was repeated.

"What? What's that you say?" the man shouted.

"Will you play cards with us?" the two shouted in return.

"Cards?" the man repeated. "Wait a while. First I must say my afternoon prayers."

The old man went through his prayers slowly and with great devotion. When he sat down the two said to him:

"Will you play now?"

"Eh? What?" the man shouted.

"Will you play cards with us now?" they shouted.

"Oh, cards!" said the man. "Just a little while—I must eat something first."

The man ordered food, ate very slowly and said grace.

"Well now," said the two, "how about a little game?"

"Eh, what?" said the man.

"A game of cards!" the two shouted.

"Oh, that!" said the man. "Yes, let's play now."

So they sat down and played; and since they were playing with a deaf opponent, the two communicated freely with each other, telling each other about their hands and advising each other on their plays. And they won without difficulty—that is to say, they won the first few games. Then their opponent began to win, and he won without interruption. Never had they witnessed such a streak of luck. At the end of two hours they were without means to continue.

"Stranger!" shouted one of the two to the elderly man. "You play cards like a shark!"

"Perhaps so," the man replied. "But why do you shout like that? Do you think I am deaf?"

PENANCE

They were two intimate friends and both of them, in a moment of weakness to which all flesh is liable, committed a grave sin—one of those sins over which it is best to throw the veil of silence. Immediately afterwards, however, they were both sincerely repentant, and they went to the rabbi and begged him for a penance which would cleanse their souls of the guilt.

"My sons," said the rabbi, "you have committed a very serious transgression, but if you will do as I say, you may hope for the grace of Heaven. Beginning today and for a whole week you are to walk about as usual, but with peas in your shoes."

Both promised to obey. At the end of the week the friends met. One of them limped painfully and showed every sign of having gone through a period of suffering. The other showed no sign of anything of the sort.

"Velvele," said the first to the second, "did you do as the rabbi ordered? You don't show any evidence of it."

"Of course, I put peas in my shoes!" replied the second. "How then? But first I boiled them."

RENEGADES AND ANTI-SEMITES

ONE WHO KNEW

The famous Orientalist, Ignaz Goldziher, was invited to a learned gathering in Budapest where the guest of honor was a certain convert who was known to have embraced Christianity in order to qualify for a professorship in the University. The professor lectured on the subject of Hungarian culture and his enthusiasm for the Magyar spirit was boundless.

"It's a pity," Goldziher remarked to the convert after the lecture, "that you were born late. You should have lived in the time of the Prophet Isaiah."

"Will you have the kindness to explain?" said the guest of honor.

And Ignaz Goldziher explained as follows:

"Isaiah denounced the Jews of his generation, telling them: 'The ox knoweth his owner and the ass his master's crib, but Israel doth not know.'* Had you been living in his day, he would have seen in Israel at least one ox who knew his owner and one ass who knew his master's crib."

A MATTER OF PRINCIPLE

In Czarist Russia a certain convert to Christianity, Necander Zussman by name, once held the official

* Isaiah, I, 3.

post of censor of Jewish books. Necander was a confirmed drunkard. In the company of a Jewish writer he once entered a tavern, and after pouring himself a large glass of liquor, he crossed himself, and drained the glass at a gulp.

His companion looked at him ruefully.

"Why," he asked, "did you have to cross yourself into the bargain?"

"That, my friend," replied the convert, "is a matter of principle with me. I do it for the sake of my fellow-Jews. Why should I give some anti-semite a chance to say that he saw a Jew drink like a fish?"

EAGER FOR A FRIEND

"Barney," said Herman to his friend, "believe it or not, I have just been baptized. I'm a Christian now."

"Well, of all —," Barney began.

"Never mind all that," Herman interrupted. "I've come to ask you to do something for me."

"Oh, really?"

"Yes, Barney, I want you to get baptized also."

Barney stared at Herman.

"I was a little in doubt before," he said at last, "but now I am sure you're crazy!"

"I'm not crazy, Barney, and I want you to do it. Do it for me!"

"But why?" Barney demanded.

"I'll tell you, Barney. It's because I want to have at least one Christian friend."

HE HELD FAST!

They told Levi Yitzchok, the famous rabbi of Berdichev, that a certain old man of seventy had become baptized.

"Lord of the Universe!" exclaimed the rabbi. "See how steadfast Thy people are to serve Thee! For seventy years that man held fast to Judaism!"

NOTHING FOR PASSOVER

He stood before the missionary, ragged and resigned, and told him he came to be baptized.

"Splendid!" cried the missionary. "Tomorrow I'll take you to the minister and he'll teach you the fundamentals of our faith!"

"Could—could you take me to-day?" asked the would-be convert.

The missionary was puzzled.

"Why?" he asked. "What's your hurry?"

"You see," was the answer, "tomorrow is Passover."

"What if it is?" asked the missionary.

"There isn't a thing in the house for Passover," the man confided, "no matzo, no wine,—nothing! I'm penniless!"

BORN AGAIN

Feitel and Feivel went together to the baptismal font, and the first to be called in was Feitel. When he came out, his friend met him eagerly.

"Nu, Feitel?" he asked.

"In the first place," replied the other with asperity, "my name is not Feitel but Philip. In the second place, I don't talk to an accursed Jew like you. You crucified our Lord!"

TIME FOR *MINCHA*

There were two in the anteroom waiting for the missionary. It was late afternoon and they had been waiting several hours.

"He takes his time, doesn't he?" remarked one of the would-be converts.

"He certainly does," the other agreed.

"Shall I tell you what I'm thinking?" said the first after a pause.

"Nu, what?"

"I'm thinking it's time for *Mincha*.

"And I too," agreed the other.

And both men stood up and recited the Afternoon Prayer.

CARLSBAD SALTS

Two Jews were strolling through a park in the Petrograd of the Czars. One of them had a residence permit in his pocket, the other didn't. Suddenly they looked up and saw a policeman ambling towards them.

The man with the permit turned to his friend:

"As soon as he is near us, I'll run. He'll go after me and you will have a chance to escape."

The policeman approached, the man with the permit ran, and the policeman ran after him. Before long the runner looked around, and making sure that his friend was out of sight, he stopped, and was seized.

"Name!" the officer demanded.

"Zelig Brodsky."

"Your permit!"

Zelig Brodsky produced his permit. The policeman examined it and became enraged: the document was in perfect order.

"What's the meaning of this?" he shouted. "Why did you try to escape?"

"I try to escape?" Zelig repeated.

"But you ran!" the officer shouted.

"Oh!" said Zelig. "I take Carlsbad salts and after taking them I have to exercise. My doctor insists."

"Why didn't you stop when you saw me chase you?"

"You chase me?" said Zelig. "It never occured to me!"

"But you saw me run, didn't you? Why did you think I ran?"

"I thought you, too, were taking Carlsbad salts!"

HOW HE KNEW

"My *poretz*," confided one Jew to another, "was in a terrible rage yesterday. Five times he wanted to slap me."

"How do you know he wanted to do it exactly five times?"

"Because I had the presence of mind to count."

"So he did slap you! Then why do you say he *wanted* to slap you?"

"Foolish question!" replied the first. "If he hadn't wanted to, would he have slapped me?"

DELICIOUS!

The chief rabbi and the cardinal sat side by side at the table. The occasion was a state banquet and the food which the management had the good taste to provide for the rabbi was kosher. But the cardinal was inclined to amuse himself and handed some of his own food to the rabbi.

"Your Eminence," said the rabbi, "don't you know we are forbidden to have non-kosher food?"

"What a pity!" replied the prelate, "it's delicious!"

As they rose from the table, the rabbi turned to the cardinal.

"Your Eminence," said he, "will you be good enough to convey my greetings to your wife?"

The cardinal drew himself up.

"Don't you know," said he, "that a priest is forbidden to have a wife?"

"What a pity!" replied the rabbi. "It's delicious!"

THE LEOPARD

Shmerel and Zelig were strolling through the streets and stopped to read a police notice in bold letters:

"A leopard escaped last night from its cage in the

menagerie," ran the notice. "Whoever comes upon the animal is obligated to kill it and notify the Police Department."

Said Shmerel to Zelig:

"I'm leaving town at once!"

"What an idea!" said Zelig. "Are you afraid you'll be killed? You are not a leopard."

"You don't understand, my friend," Shmerel explained. "They'll kill you first and then how are you going to prove you are not a leopard?"

"OPERATE OPERATE"

From his wife who was taking the cure in a place across the border, a husband received a telegram reading as follows: "Says to operate operate." To which the husband sent a telegram in reply reading: "Says to operate operate."

Several days later the man was summoned to police headquarters. The police-chief confronted him with copies of both telegrams and demanded to know what sort of correspondence he was conducting with persons across the border.

"It's plain," said the official, "that you are using a secret code."

"Your Excellency," pleaded the man, "this is no code! This—"

"Your denial won't help you!" the police-chief declared. "We know a code when we see one. The best thing for you to do is to confess!"

"Let me read the telegrams to you, Your Excellency!"

"Are you implying that we can't read?"

"No, but these telegrams, Your Excellency—"

"Then go ahead and read them!"

"You see, Your Excellency, my wife is ill, and before she left we arranged that she would go to a surgeon. She did so and sent me this telegram: 'Says to operate. Operate?' And I replied: 'Says to operate? Operate!' "

EN ROUTE

MAZEL TOV!

A new passenger entered the compartment and found every seat occupied. There was an old woman, however, who was in possession of two seats and preparing to take a nap.

"*Mazel tov,* grandmother!" said the passenger to the lady.

She thanked him and moved over to make room for the courteous stranger, who sat down beside her.

"A *mazel tov* is always welcome," said she, "but what's the occasion?"

The man made himself altogether comfortable.

"You see," he explained, "this is the first time I've seen you since your wedding."

A CONVERSATION

The two travelers found themselves in the same compartment and recognizing a co-religionist in each other, they wanted very much to engage in conversation, but hesitated. Each perceived in the other a certain aloofness and feared that the attempt might meet with rebuff.

At last one of the travelers expressed himself.

"Oy!" he groaned.

The other responded immediately.

"You're right!" he exclaimed. "That's exactly what I've been thinking!"

ANOTHER CONVERSATION

In the case of another pair of travelers, conversation moved much more smoothly.

"Where, may I ask, do you come from?" asked one.

"Of course you may ask," replied the other. "I come from Warsaw and I'm going to Vilna. My business is dry-goods—retail. My first name is Gimpel, my family name is Abramowitz. I'm neither rich nor poor, just average. I have two sons, both married. Yes, I have daughters also—three of them, one is married, one is engaged, and the third is not yet of age. I've no hobbies, I'm not looking for any new line of business, I don't take snuff, I don't smoke, I know nothing about politics. If I've forgotten anything, be kind enough to ask me now. I really would like to take a nap."

CONFIDENCE FOR CONFIDENCE

They were fellow passengers on board an ocean liner, both Jews, one a hunchback, the other endowed with the tell-tale nose. For a few days the second avoided his fellow-Jew. In the end, however, he made up to the hunchback.

"My friend," said he with the nose one day, "I'm going to impart a little confidence to you. I'm a Jew."

"Confidence for confidence," said the other. "I'm a hunchback."

WISE AND SIMPLE

"May I ask," said a passenger with a philosophic turn of mind to his neighbor, "where you are going?"

"I'm going far," replied the other.

"That's how it is," mused the first, "the only place where we are happy is the place where we are not."

"Yes," said the other, "that's where I am going."

HE LIED!

In the railway coach Shmerel met his friend Berel.

"Where are you going?" asked Shmerel.

"To Grodno," said Berel.

Shmerel became indignant.

"You're telling me you are going to Grodno so as to have me think you are going to Vilna. But I know you are really going to Grodno, so what's the idea of lying about it?"

THEY LOOKED AT EACH OTHER

"You know," said a returned traveler to his friend, "on the trip from Warsaw to Lodz the conductor looked at me very queerly."

"Just how did he look at you?" asked the friend.

"He looked at me as if I had no ticket."

"So what did you do?"

"What could I do? I looked at him as if I had one!"

SAME COLOR

They were two strangers in a first class compartment of a railroad car and one of them lighted a cigar.

"Smoking is not allowed here!" said the other testily.

"I know it," replied the smoker calmly and continued to puff away.

The second traveler called the conductor.

"He is violating the rules," he complained. "This compartment is reserved for non-smokers."

"And I say," replied the smoker, "that it's he who is violating the rules. He is travelling in a first-class compartment on a second-class ticket."

The accusing passenger turned pale and went out hastily.

On the platform of the station the two met again. The curiosity of the non-smoker overcame his resentment.

"Are you a clairvoyant?" he asked his fellow-passenger. "How did you know I had a second-class ticket?"

"I'm no clairvoyant," replied the other, "I saw a corner of your ticket stick out of your pocket and it was the same color as mine."

GLOSSARY

Aineni yodeah (Hebrew), I don't know

Baal-agalah, wagoner

Baigel, roll shaped like a ring

Bimah, platform or pulpit

Cholileh, God forbid!

Chutzpah, effrontery

Forverts (Forward), Yiddish daily published in New York

Ganev, thief

Gazlon, brigand

Gimmel, third letter of the Hebrew alphabet, pronounced like the g in "get"

Ibn Ezra, Abraham, scholar, poet, and philosopher (1092-1167)

Kaftan, long black coat worn by East European Jews.

Kaptzen, poor man

Kol Nidre, the prayer that ushers in the services on Yom Kippur eve

Korah, led a revolt against Moses in the desert; a man of high station and wealth (Numbers, XVI)

Landsman, countryman

Litvak, Lithuanian Jew; crafty fellow

Maggid, preacher

Menorath Hamoar, "The Candlestick of Light," a popular religious work by Isaac Aboab (lived in Spain about the year 1300)

Mincha, afternoon prayers

Poretz, Polish squire

Rosh Hashanah, the New Year festival

Shadchen, marriage broker

Shammes, sexton

Shlemiel, ne'er-do-well

Shnorrer, beggar

Shofar, ram's horn, blown during the New Year's service

Sholem Aleichem, peace unto you! (Greeting)

Talis, prayer-shawl

Tefillin, phylacteries

Tippesh, dolt

Yeshuvnik, village resident

Yichus, high lineage; family pride

Yom Kippur, Day of Atonement